Eggs to lay, chickens to hatch

Previous praise for Chris van Wyk

'Chris van Wyk…tells us more about South Africa than a shelf of self-justifying tomes. Supremely Van Wyk reminds us that the lives and actions of so-called ordinary people have as great an influence on history as those of the so-called great.' – *Darryl Accone, Mail & Guardian Books Editor*

'Van Wyk's strength is to look at the world as if with the innocent eyes of a child and to convey this hopeful vision to others, to recapture the resilience of childhood so that it is not lost but continues, to shape adult existence and to fortify our collective sense of self.' – *Sowetan*

'Where it rumbles with fury, laughter comes as a release. In a phrase, it is a controlled and deliberate account, bursting with life.' – *Sunday Independent*

'It's the amazing sense of place and time that Van Wyk brings to his childhood memoir that raises *Shirley, Goodness & Mercy* a cut above many other books in this genre.' – *Cape Times*

Eggs to lay,
chickens to hatch

A memoir

Chris van Wyk

Picador Africa

First published in 2010 by Picador Africa,
an imprint of Pan Macmillan South Africa
Private Bag X19, Northlands
Johannesburg, 2116

www.panmacmillan.co.za
www.picadorafrica.co.za

ISBN 978-1-77010-173-9

The names and surnames of some of the characters have been changed to protect their privacy.

My name is Selina Mabiletsa (see pages 277–79) was published in 1996 by ViVa Books
(PO Box 28510, Kensington, 2101, South Africa).

At the time of going to print, permission was being sought for the following copyright
permissions: the two lines (on page 13) from 'That Old Black Magic', written by Johnny
Mercer; the four lines (on page 61) from 'Only the Lonely', written by Joe Melson and Roy
Orbison; the five lines (on page 61) from 'Moon River', written by Johnny Mercer; the four
lines (on page 253) from 'Sylvia's Mother', written by Shel Silverstein; and the eight lines
(on page 288) from 'Ain't Nobody Here but us Chickens', written by Alex Kramer and Joan
Whitney.

Editing by Andrea Nattrass
Proofreading by Sally Hines
Design and typesetting by Rockbottom graphic&design
Cover design by K4
Front cover photograph of Agnes Msiza by Keith Hendricks
Front cover photograph of Riverlea house by Anneliese Peters
Back cover photograph of Chris van Wyk by Cedric Nunn
Front and back flap photographs supplied by Chris van Wyk
Back flap photograph of radio by Dmitry Poliansky

Printed by Ultra Litho (Pty) Limited

For Kevin and Karl

It takes a village to raise a child.

African proverb

A message in the wind

The other day I received a phone call from a Ms Smith, a teacher at Kloof Primary School in Johannesburg. She asked me if I would come and talk to her Grade 7s about *A message in the wind.*

'*A message in the wind?*' I asked. I get requests from schools all the time – to talk to kids about poetry, the importance of reading, freedom fighters such as Nelson Mandela and Beyers Naudé – but never about *A message in the wind.*

A message in the wind is the second book I wrote and the first for children. It's not the best book I've ever written, and yet it remains one of my favourites. I was young and eager – twenty-three years old – and knew very little about the art of writing.

I wrote the book in 1980. I was newly married and newly jobless and my wife Kathy and I were living at her mother's house in Riverlea. One day I saw an advert in some magazine. 'Write a children's novel and win R3 000.'

Why not, I thought. So, every morning, after Kathy and her mother left for work, I would get up and clean our room, have breakfast, wash dishes. Then I'd sit at the dining room table with my ballpoint pens and foolscap paper and get to work. There were no computers then, and I couldn't afford a typewriter.

What came out of my head went something like this: Vusi and Robert, both about twelve years old, are two black South African friends but from different tribes. These two tribes are enemies in the present time, but their hostility goes back to a mysterious feud that happened hundreds of years ago. Vusi and Robert would like to know what that feud was all about.

1

One day during their school holidays, Vusi and Robert find themselves messing about in the veld, as boys do, looking around and throwing stones at tin cans. They come across an old bath-tub, and, of all things, a light plane that had crashed!

This surprise find gives them an idea: to build a time machine! And what would they do with such a thing? Yes, you guessed – travel into the past to find out why their ancestors became enemies.

So they cart their treasure to Robert's backyard where they get to work. Every afternoon, for a week or so, there's a banging and a chopping and a drilling and a screwing. And there it is: a bath-tub with an aircraft engine and three or four clocks as the dashboard. A time machine.

This is my favourite page of the book which describes what happens next:

Then, on the last day, when they fitted the final screw, the last wire, it began to rain. Even their spirits were drenched.

'Well, it's done,' Vusi shouted above the loud patter.

'Well, let's get inside and try it,' suggested Vusi.

'Okay,' Robert agreed. The two boys climbed into the bath, out of the pouring rain. Robert began to fiddle with the knobs and dials.

'Well?' Vusi asked.

'Well, nothing,' said Robert, embarrassed.

'At least it's stopped raining,' Vusi consoled his friend. Robert fiddled again.

'Hey!' Vusi nudged his friend.

'What's wrong?' Robert asked.

'It's dry outside.'

'So?'

'It's dry! It's not supposed to be ... it was raining ...'

'Robert stared outside. 'Yes!' he exclaimed.

'You know what that means?' Vusi shouted excitedly.

'Perhaps,' said Robert. 'But let's try again.'

Robert fiddled with the knobs once more. Suddenly the rain was thundering down.

'We were in the past!' shouted Vusi.

'Yes,' cried Robert. 'We were back to before it rained.'

The two boys jumped out of the spacecraft and began to laugh and dance and cry in the rain. Mrs Nhlabatsi, the neighbour, peered over the fence, her face wet and angry.

'Stop that noise, you foolish animals. My baby's sleeping!'

'Yes, Mama!' The two boys stopped immediately, feeling sheepish.

'And I hope you two have finished all that banging and knocking!'

'We were just killing time, Mama,' Robert explained.

Ms Smith tells me that she has been teaching the book to her Grade 7s for five or six years. And they love the story.

'So, will you come and talk to them about the book?' she asks.

'Of course!'

So, one Thursday morning, I find myself standing on the podium in the assembly hall, watching as three classrooms of twelve-year-old boys and girls troop into the hall with their teachers trying, without much success, to keep them quiet.

I watch their nudging and giggling and ear pulling, and it all takes me back to my own childhood. Eventually their teachers get them to sit down – cross-legged on the wooden floor, and keep, almost, quiet. Then a boy farts and the noise begins all over again.

A joke pops into my head which I want to share with the kids: Is there a message in the wind? I want to ask the boys. But when I note the looks of embarrassment on the faces of the teachers, I decide not to tell the joke.

After my talk about my little novel, I decide to play a game with the kids.

'If you could travel back in time,' I ask them, 'what would you do, where would you go, what would you change?'

The hands fly up and I choose five or six random boys and girls.

'I would go and visit Nelson Mandela when he was my age – and tell him that he would be president one day.'

'I wouldn't go far,' a boy says. 'I would go to a time when I could see the Lotto numbers, play them and win twenty million rand.'

'But to do that you'd have to travel into the future,' I point out.

He's ready for this problem. 'I'll travel to a Saturday when the Lotto numbers are announced, make sure it's one where there's been no winner. I'd write down the numbers. And then I'd just travel two more days back and play those numbers.'

'And you're a millionaire.'

From the dozens of hands I choose a serious-looking boy.

'I would go back to a time when my father was still alive,' he says. 'And then I would spend much more time with him than I did.'

This gets us all quiet for a few seconds as we think about time and opportunities and life.

'And what about you, sir?' one of them asks.

'Me?'

'Yes, sir!' shouts a chorus of learners.

I probably would change some moments of my life: mistakes, unnecessary arguments. I would work harder at school, not become a smoker, not embarrass myself.

WRITING A MEMOIR is a little like travelling into your own past. Unlike science fiction, you can't change the past. But, like science fiction, it does have its own magic.

Grace

When I went to bed last night, the last person I saw was my ma. Now it's the next morning. I open my eyes and the first person I see is Grace. Ma has gone to the factory to work. Grace is here to work – scrub the floors, iron clothes, wash dishes, make the beds. And, this afternoon before she leaves, wash me!

Why doesn't Grace go to the factory and Ma stay here and work, I wonder? Then I could be with Ma in the daytime too. But I also like Grace. She's black. She wears a yellow doek which she ties in a thick knot at the back of her head. I know this knot well because I fiddle with it when she abbas me.

When she wakes me, I don't see her face or her teeth with the gap in the bottom row, because she has already turned away to make my mother's and father's bed.

'D'you want to go to a party?' she says.

'Huh?'

'A party,' she nods. 'And eat sweets.'

'Is it my birthday?'

'No!' she laughs.

I had a birthday just the other day. There were four candles on the cake, lit up! I had to blow them out. There was a horse on the cake and a man on the horse and a hat on the man.

'Come.' She pulls my arms and legs out of flannel pyjamas and puts them into cotton shorts and a shirt.

(I must interrupt my story to tell you: when all this happened I didn't know a lot of the words for the things I saw and felt and saw people do – 'pyjamas' I knew, but not 'flannel', 'accomplice', 'epaulette'. The words came later, every day, one by one.)

5

I pee, brush my teeth. I eat mealiemeal porridge with sugar and butter and milk – it's delicious, but a party's nicer. I ask about the party.

'Will there be sweets?'

'Ja.' She wipes porridge from my face.

We're out of the house and she locks the door and we're in a courtyard. She sees not one, not two, but three of her friends, all housekeepers. Two are hanging up washing and one is sweeping a red stoep. They all stop their work – and my heart sinks. Grace doesn't understand what happens at parties – there'll be children and children love sweets. They stuff them in their mouths and their pockets and nobody ever says, 'Let's leave some for Chris.'

Here in the courtyard it's a four-way conversation, loud, and everything someone says seems to make the other three laugh or go 'Awu batho'.

Then Grace puts me on her back and we're off, out of the courtyard and down the street.

It's late January and overcast. Still, there are lots of interesting things to look at, sniff at and listen to: women coming out of shops with loaves of bread under their arms, a man on a bicycle ringing his bell…it puts me in the party mood.

Around a corner and there it is. It must be – there're lots of kids, my age, older. And there's a big noise, calling and shoving and 'that way' and 'this way'.

A lady barks out an instruction and we stand in a line.

'Why are we standing like this?' I ask Grace.

'For the sweets.'

It's unusual but if that's what they want us to do for a sweet, I'll do it.

Another instruction: 'Left arm!'

All around me, kids' sleeves are being pushed up. Grace helps me push up mine.

Up there at the start of the line a woman makes her way from arm to arm. I watch her. She works quickly, spending less than a second or two on each arm – what is she doing?

She's wearing a white dress with epaulettes and toney red shoes – it's a kind of a uniform but I can't place it. She stops by me and rubs something onto my arm with cotton wool. It's cold and has a sharp smell. I don't know what it is but in the years to come I'll smell it in hospitals and it will remind me of this day. It's spirits! And this woman, I suddenly realise, is no ordinary woman, she's an evil woman. A nurse!

But it's too late! There's another one following her – same dress, epaulettes and shoes – and this one has a needle. And before I can withdraw my arm she plunges the needle into my arm – ah!

I feel pain and humiliation. There will be no sweets, no chocolates, no cake. No party. Grace has betrayed me.

By the time Ma comes home from work, the pain has left my arm, together with the smell of spirits. But the humiliation returns, complete with two fresh rows of tears.

'She told me we were going to a party!' I bawl.

But Ma is not sympathetic and Grace is not contrite. Instead they both laugh. And I begin to realise that my own mother was an accomplice.

'If Grace had told you that you were gonna get a vaccination would you have gone?'

'Yes,' I say, but it is such a weak yes that even I am not convinced. And it makes Ma and Grace laugh a little bit more.

WE MOVED TO Riverlea soon afterwards.

We left Newclare at night, on a lorry packed with our stuff.

We left the old houses that stood right up against each other in rows and rows, the red stoeps that at age four seemed as high and as dangerous as cliffs, the shops where the sweets were piled behind glass, each kind in its own glass house – and still more in giant glass jars on top of the counter so that a boy could only see sweets no matter where he looked. We left that school where instead of a party there was once a vaccination festival.

We left Grace. She didn't come with us to Riverlea. I asked Ma why.

'Grace has got other plans,' Ma said.

'Who's gonna look after me now?'

Ma said, 'Don't worry, I'll find somebody. That's the least of our problems.'

Actually, what Ma – and many other mothers – did not realise at the time was that it was far from the least of our problems.

A woman could help shape a boy's life while she ironed his shirts, buttered his bread and made his bed.

Agnes did that for me. But I'm going to have to wait a few years before she appears on our doorstep.

A matchbox

My plan was to stay awake all the time – for about a hundred and some odd hours. To stay awake on the lorry and take in with my eyes and ears and nose the dark factories and long steely railway line, the bridge and the people walking across it, the cars and their yellow headlights…But I fell asleep because suddenly it was daylight and I was awake in the new house. Riverlea.

After Newclare, the spaces between the houses seem too wide.

There are rows and rows and rows of houses, too many to count. Matchboxes, they will be called in time.

Ma and Dad don't seem very happy with the size of our new home. Two tiny bedrooms, a bathroom and toilet in one 'room', a small kitchen and a mini lounge.

'And look at these walls,' one of our new neighbours says, 'so thin your neighbours can hear you change your mind.'

In no time, everybody's repeating the same joke. It seems the walls are so thin you can hear someone telling a joke.

Goodyear

'Mr van Wyk!'

That's my ma calling me. And when she calls me that, I know she wants me to do her a favour.

It's June 1963. Ma works in a factory. But she's home now because she's going to have another baby. It's called maternity leave.

My friends and I all own posh cars. I drive a Mercedes Benz. The cars are old, discarded bicycle wheels with the tyre and spokes removed, and driven with a clothes hanger bent this way and that way until it looks like a U with a handle. You curl the U up against the rolling wheel and away you go. Ten, twenty cars make one deafening, screeching noise as we drive up and down the dusty streets.

A much quieter car is an old car tyre. To drive this one, all you do is push the tyre and run behind it, slapping it to the left or right to steer it.

Ma wants me to go to the shop for her. She opens our front door and stands in the doorway, above the three steps that would take her down into our dusty front yard. She is very light-skinned, like a white lady almost. And her stomach is a big balloon.

'Mr van Wyk!'

I drive my car into the yard. 'Excuse me, sir,' she says, as I come to a halt by the stoep.

'Hullo, ma'm,' I greet politely. 'What can I do for you?'

'What a nice car! What's it called?'

'Mercedes Benz 380S…'

'Ooh, I beg your pardon!'

'… 296 litre.'

'You don't say,' she says, her eyes growing bigger and bigger.

'Pty.'

'Wow!'

I can't think of any more letters and numbers to add onto my Mercedes. I look down at the smooth tyre and all it says, faintly, is GOODYEAR.

'Is this car fast?' she wants to know.

'Very. Sixty miles per hour.'

'Well, I'm dying for a cigarette and I need a car like this to go to the shops. Do you think…?'

'Hand over the cash, lady.'

Ma hands me the twenty cents. The cigarettes are nineteen cents for a pack of twenty. As I drive away she calls: 'Keep the change for petrol!'

And I'm off.

RIVERLEA HAS FILLED up very fast since the day we arrived a couple of years ago. When we came we were the only people in our street. Then the trucks kept rolling in, every day, bringing people and their furniture.

Now I've got so many friends and I can't even remember how we first met. I can't say, 'I first met Toolbag when I saw him throwing away stuff in their dustbin, or I first saw Marlon when he ran past our house with his dog Jacko. Or I first saw Auntie Vera when she asked me to help her up our front steps because she was a little drunk.

It just feels like I've known these people all my life.

And talk of the devil. As I race down Colorado Drive towards the shop, I hear: 'Christopher!'

It's Ma's friend, Auntie Vera, calling me.

I catch brakes and look over her garden fence at her standing in her doorway, like Ma did five minutes ago. Mothers are always standing in their doorways as if they're scared to come out of their own homes. I think it's because there's always a kettle boiling or a baby crying or a pot on the stove that has to be watched.

'Are you going to the shops?' she calls in her tiny voice.

'Excuse me, Auntie Vera?' I say with a little puzzled frown on my face – although I've heard her perfectly. I even know that she wants me to go to the shops for her too. But I pretend that I know nothing.

'The shops,' she says.

'Yes, Auntie Vera.'

She gestures with her little hand that I should come to her. I go.

'Please, can you get these for your auntie.'

'These' is a list of things and I'll write it exactly the way she has – on a torn-off lid of a cigarette box:

half loaf of bread
Sterivita milk
Sml tin pilchids (in cheeli)
20 cigarets

I don't know why she doesn't look on the pilchard tin to see how it's spelt. As for 'cigarets': she smokes Stuyvesant and I don't think she's ever going to get that one right.

But right now I'm not worried about spelling. Something else is bothering me. I was driving my car to the shop to buy Ma's cigarettes. That means I buy the cigarettes, I put the pack in my pocket, I buy Chappies with the one cent change and stuff that into my mouth. And then I still have my two hands free to drive my car home.

But now I've got this list of things and how will I drive? I look at the list and I look at my car…

'You can leave the tyre here in my yard.'

It's a Mercedes Benz and she calls it a tyre! And what's more, she thinks she's doing me a favour by letting me park my car in her yard. But in actual fact, *I'm* the one doing *her* a favour.

People of Riverlea! They take advantage of a person.

Dustbin and wife

Auntie Vera is 'saved' – again. She says: 'I have accepted the Lord Jesus Christ as my own personal saviour.'

How do I know this? Because I was in the kitchen eavesdropping when she told Ma. She's been saved about ten times in the last year.

Auntie Vera and her husband Uncle Royce are not really our uncle and aunt, they're just our neighbours.

Auntie Vera has a tiny, squeaky voice. Sometimes, when Ma and Dad are at work, we take one of Dad's Frank Sinatra LPs and play it at 45 rpm rather than 33 rpm. Instead of hearing Sinatra we hear Auntie Vera singing:

> *That old black magic has me in its spell*
> *That old black magic that you weave so well…*

Then we take it in turns standing on the couch and doing an impersonation of Auntie Vera. No matter how many times we do this, we end up collapsing on the couch laughing until the tears run down.

She's as small as Minnie Mouse, about five foot one inch. Uncle Royce is about two inches taller. They don't have any children. I think that's because they were scared their children might grow taller than them and step on them by accident – or on purpose.

Uncle Royce works in a furniture factory in Doornfontein with Dad. He's very fair with sleek black hair and has an all-day grin on his face. He laughs a lot and makes my dad laugh too.

He has one special joke which he only tells Auntie Vera and only when she's frying fish for supper. He smells the fish when he comes home from work as he approaches their front door. This makes him happy because he likes fish. He knocks on the door, slowly removes his checked Ayers and Smith cap. And when Auntie Vera opens the door, he says:

'Darling, I've been working in water all day – I feel like a piece of fish.'

They both burst out laughing as if it's the first time he's ever told the joke.

Auntie Vera often comes over for tea and some skinder. When she's in a good mood she refers to Uncle Royce as 'my dustbin' (because it rhymes with 'husband').

When Auntie Vera's not saved – she calls it being lapsed – she gets as drunk as Uncle Royce. Then she comes over to us and cries her heart out to Ma – snot en trane.

This usually happens on a Saturday evening and then the normal Saturday evening Van Wyk routines are disrupted. Like, for instance, we can't listen to the radio because it's in the lounge where Ma and Auntie Vera are having their skinder, or Ma doesn't play rummy with us.

Ma closes the lounge door so that we can't see her friend because she's stumbling all over our furniture and she looks a sight. And Ma doesn't want us to hear what she has to say about her dustbin. But Ma doesn't have to worry. Even with the door open it's hard to hear what she's saying; it comes out all jumbled up. The only things I can hear are, 'Am I right or wrong, Shirl?' 'Is it fair, Shirl?'

Ma just says, 'You're right, Vera. No, you got a point.' Ma also says, 'Watch that cigarette, you're gonna burn the couch.'

Auntie Vera is having such a good time sobbing that soon she's looking for a drink. And this is the part that my brother Derek and I like. Ma comes into the bedroom and tells us to go to Auntie Mammie's for a nip of brandy.

'But Ma, you said you don't want us going to no shebeen for nobody.'

'Ag come, boys,' Auntie Vera squeaks. 'For your auntie.'

'If yous go quickly,' Ma says. 'yous can keep the change.'

That's what we wanted to hear.

It's dark outside – I know it's past seven o'clock because I can hear Paddy O'Byrne reading the news on the radios where the doors are open. First we buy the nip at Auntie Mammie's, where there's a lot of drinking and jiving going on. Then we head for Boeta Issy's spaza shop in Ganges Street.

As we pass under a street lamp, Derek turns to me and says, 'Is this an adventure that we're having?'

I think about it first: one minute we're in bed and the next we're in a shebeen seeing people dancing and shouting and using filthy language. And now we're on our way to buy comics!

'Yes it is,' I nod. 'Definitely.'

He giggles and the sweat on his nose glows under the lamplight.

Boeta Issy's spaza shop is the best. There are lots of spaza shops that sell sweets. But Boeta Issy sells sweets *and* comics. Bubblegum and *Batman*, Sharps and *Spiderman*, Tiger Toffees and *Tarzan*.

Boeta Issy is a Muslim and I hear they never allow alcohol in their homes. Well, if he only knew what I have stuck in my coat pocket!

We return half an hour later. Auntie Vera's happy because now she's got brandy and she can sob some more and tell Ma how sad she is. We're happy because we've got comics and bubblegum. Ma's just relieved that we're back home.

We lie in our bed trying to read about Batman and Spiderman, but the sounds of Sobbingwoman coming from the lounge won't let us get very far.

'She's gonna pass out here,' Derek says. 'She's too drunk to walk back home.'

I nod from over the top of my comic.

'Where will she sleep?'

We think about that for a while.

'I know,' I say. 'I'll put my pillow on the floor and she can sleep on it.'

We explode into giggles and Ma comes into the room and glares at us because we're being rude. But we're ready for her. We hold up our comics and say, 'Jislaaik, Ma, this Sad Sack is funny.'

Ma waves a threatening finger at us, then goes back to the lounge to make sure Auntie Vera hasn't burnt down our couch.

'Where's Uncle Royce?' Derek asks.

'Shh,' I say, holding a finger to my lips.

'What?'

'I think he's under the bed listening to us.'

Snakes and ladders for Christmas

Ma prepares for Christmas in January already!

She goes to Adams, a store in Doornfontein, a few blocks away from the clothing factory where she works. On the store window it says: ADAMS GENERAL DEALER. You go inside and all you see is stuff: pots, pans, cups and saucers, linoleum, plastic tablecloths, tricycles and bicycles, footballs, jigsaw puzzles. Mr Adams has so many things that he has to hang half of them from the ceiling and the walls.

It's hard to find Mr Adams himself among all this. But he's always there somewhere, bearded, Bic ballpoint pen in hand, scribbling away in a receipt book so dog-eared that my teacher Mrs Abrahams would give him six of the best if he ever tried to bring that book within a mile of our school gate.

He wears a woollen kufia all year round. His face, like his shop, is full of stuff: two thick sideburns, a beard and a moustache the colour of steel wool. They all grow and flow into one so that it looks like he's wearing a balaclava. His brown eyes dart all over the place, at his goods and at the customers who come in to buy them.

He greets Ma with a quick smile that is gone in an instant. Mr Adams hasn't got time to stand around smiling all day.

Ma asks him if the new catalogue is ready yet.

'Long ago, man,' he says. A hand slips down behind the counter and comes up with one brand new Christmas Catalogue 1967.

(It's not so 'long ago' mind you. Ma was here last week and it wasn't ready then.)

Ma brings it home and we all dive for it.

Ma says: 'Hey, hold it, hold it! It's only January and already yous wanna mess the book up!'

Derek (eight years old) gets it first and the rest of us, me (ten), Shaune (five) and Alison (two), have to make do with looking at it from over his shoulders. This is not an ideal way for me: Derek is in charge and he turns the pages whether I'm ready or not.

Derek is sitting at the kitchen table, Ma is busy cooking and our eyes are stinging from the onions braising in a pot on the stove. The rest of the house is empty. In the lounge Springbok Radio is talking and talking but nobody's there to listen.

This catalogue is a glossy photo album of some of the stuff Mr Adams has in his shop. The last two pages have little squares numbered from one to one hundred, like a Snakes and Ladders game without the pictures of snakes and ladders. These squares are for the stamps which are twenty-five cents each.

Block number one has a picture of the stamp in it – a free stamp to sort of give you a kick-start. Ma says it's a facsimile. I like that word and I say it over and over again. It's funny that even a free stamp in the corner of a book has a fancy name.

Each picture in the catalogue has the price of the item in one corner and the number of stamps you need in another corner. Let's say the set of cups and saucers costs twenty rand. In one corner it will say 'R20.00' and in the other '80 stamps'.

The biggest, grandest picture of all is the 32-Piece Dinner Service – arranged all nice and symmetrical, like my father's football team photo. The oval plate in the centre – the goalie. And then the plates, then the side plates and last but not least the saucers.

'Is Ma gonna buy the dinner serve us?' Alison wants to know.

'The what, baby?' Ma says, trying to hide her laughter.

My sister senses she's said something wrong and now she won't repeat it. She hides underneath the kitchen table, but Ma won't give up and coaxes it out of her.

'The dinner serve us.'

'Come here, you sweetie,' Ma says, laughing out loud now, and gives her a hug.

But Ma hasn't answered Alison's question. I think it's because the 'serve us' costs twenty times her weekly wages, which is sixteen rand and fifty-three cents per week.

Every Friday Ma gets her wages and, first thing she does, she stops by at Adams and buys two stamps. She comes home, takes out the catalogue, licks the stamps and sticks them down onto the squares. Ma's aim is to buy a set of pots and a set of cups and saucers. If she buys two stamps every week she'll make it for Christmas with a few weeks to spare.

But getting those stamps is like Snakes and Ladders in more ways than one. One week Ma wins on the fahfee so she can buy four stamps instead of only two. It's like landing on a ladder and going up, skipping a few squares. A few weeks later, Derek needs new school shoes and Ma has to pay the rent. This makes Ma short of cash this week, so the stamps have to wait: it's like being swallowed by the snake on number twenty-one and having to go back to number fifteen.

PERSONALLY I DON'T think Christmas will ever come. It's too far away. And between January and Christmas there's a piece of summer at either end and there's winter in the middle...

But suddenly it's early December. School's closed for six weeks and everywhere you go mothers and fathers are stressing and saying:

'Oh God, what am I going to do? Christmas is just around the corner!'

'I hope we can paint the house this year and I wouldn't mind one of those new hi-fi radios and Christmas is just around the corner.'

'Ai junne! I just started this new job a few weeks ago, so I can forget about holiday pay – and Christmas is just around the corner.'

One Saturday morning, Christmas being just around the corner, Ma takes us shopping for our Christmas clothes: me,

Derek and Shaune. (Alison's still too tiny so Ma just buys her a pretty dress and shoes and brings them home.)

Ma makes sure we're all clean, especially our necks and feet because we're going to fit on shirts and shoes and Ma says she doesn't want to be embarrassed right there in the shops.

Ma is wearing her black skirt and white blouse with the frills in front that flutter in the breeze. Her lips are painted red and it makes her look like she's going off to war. When she scolds us now her words fly through a red mouth and scare us.

We get on to the Putco bus and Ma says to the driver, 'One and two halves.' Shaune is not at school yet so he rides for free.

The bus is full of other mothers and their children. The mothers are all smoking cigarettes and saying to each other: 'Ai, can yous believe it; it's like we just took the trimmings off yesterday and it's Christmas again.'

The little girls are smiling and chewing musk-flavoured Beechies. They bounce up and down on their seats as they describe dresses they once gazed at in the shop windows of their dreams but which they will soon be wearing.

We boys give our friends a little nudge and say: 'Ja, sonny.' We don't say more than that because our mothers are listening, ready to correct every sentence ('not "der people did come" – "the people came"') or ('don't call him "Jiga", his name is James').

When we get off the bus in town, Ma says, 'Hold hands!'

Me, Shaune and Derek hold hands and we don't have to ask why. There are about a million people all around us, rushing off to a shop or a bus stop. And to make you more deurmekaar there's pop music screaming from shops and record bars all around you. To make sure we don't let go of each other Ma tells us that every year, around this time, about a hundred children get lost in town. After a couple of days wandering about without food, a kind mother takes you home with her, to Soweto. You have to learn a new language, like Zulu, which is ten times harder than English. Your Zulu mother also then changes your name to Siphowena or something that you can't even pronounce.

'So don't let go,' Ma says.

I don't let go. But it's not easy holding hands in town and it's going to lead to arguments and Ma knows that. She says:

'And no fighting, do yous hear me?'

But there's no way we're not gonna fight and, sure enough, it starts when we pass the City Hall and spot Father Christmas. Shaune wants to stop and stare at him until Easter, but Derek and I want to get a move on and we need his hands.

Derek and I pull and Shaune lets out a scream, louder than the music and the traffic combined.

Ma swings around and says:

'*What* are yous doing to the *child!*'

'Nothing, Ma. He wants to…'

'Embarrass me in town OK? Just embarrass me!'

Pritchard, Market and President streets are lined with shops that say 'Outfitters' on the window. All the mannequins are pink, with no hair and eyes, but are dressed in the latest fashions. We go into Haroon's Outfitters. It smells like new shoes and new shirts and new pants. Young Indian men are everywhere, looking busy and important with tape measures around their necks like the doctors at Corrie Hospital with their stethoscopes.

Two of them come up to Ma and the Sizes and Colours Show begins starring Shirley and Sons. Ma starts rattling things off.

'He takes a size nine, he's a 'leven and a half, he's a thirteen.'

'Do you have this in blue?'

'There's almost no hem in this…They'll outgrow it too quickly. It's for Christmas but also for Sundays.'

'This is nice but do you have it in a four?'

'These two have a lining but this one…what about this one?'

The Indian men are jumping about like Apaches around a fire, determined to please Ma.

I fit on new shoes. Ma's got tiny feet; up to last Christmas she used to try on my shoes because we took the same size. Now she fits on Derek's. Ma tells me to take a few steps in the new shoes, five paces there, five back.

'Do they hurt?'

'No, Ma.'

'Are you sure?' She makes her eyes go big when she asks this.

'Yes, Ma.'

'Come here.'

I go up to her and she squeezes the tip of the new shoe with her thumb.

'Your toe is right here at the end. Are you sure you're comfortable?'

'Yes, Ma.'

Then it's Derek's turn. Ma and the salesman repeat the whole routine. But I'm not listening because actually my new shoes do feel a little tight. Ma will go mad if I tell her now. I'll wear these shoes on Christmas day, but I won't go out, I'll stay inside the whole day and Ma will say, 'Now what's the matter with you?' I'll just say, 'Nothing.' I'll…

'Ma…'

'I knew it!' Ma says.

The salesman fetches a bigger pair.

The wait is over

The wait for Christmas is unbearable. On the radio Elvis, Cliff Richard and Johnny Mathis are all singing Christmas songs about mistletoe and holly and reindeer.

There are about three days to go and it's time to do a 'spring clean'. We pile all the furniture into the yard: the whole year the bugs have been eating us alive and now it's time for revenge. We spray Doom on the mattresses and bedsprings and watch the little bloodsuckers scatter out of their secret holes, one long stripe of bugs rushing as if there's a Christmas sale on blood at the OK Bazaars. But they die on the way. Last night when they were eating us alive they didn't know that Doomsday was just around the corner.

The bugs remind me of the gwarra sessions that we have in the street. Me and Derek and Rathead, Toolbag, the Jackson brothers Hippie and Pikkie, Marlon and Crowbar.

Gwarra means 'to tease' and it's a teasing contest between two boys for the entertainment of the rest. This usually takes place in the afternoons after school when the soccer ball's got a puncture or we kicked it into Mrs Brodie's yard and she doesn't want to give it back.

It goes something like this:

'Sonny, you guys are so many in the house, yous eat in shifts.'

'Yous are so poor, when your house was burgled yesterday the burglars brought you some furniture.'

As we fumigate now, I remember what Toolbag said to Rathead:

'Sonny, your house is so filthy, even the bugs walk around in dustcoats.'

And as I look at these bugs, running for their lives, I think they wish they had gas masks rather than dustcoats.

Everybody's in a good mood and so am I. But my friend Marlon Myburgh, from next door, makes me stop being happy for a moment. Marlon is two years older than me, but we're in the same class because he sort of struggles at school and gets a lot of things wrong.

One day I heard Marlon's dad tell my dad about Marlon's poor grades. He said, 'The laaitie battles', and somehow that didn't sound too bad.

Marlon is well built and handsome – according to girls who know about stuff like that. He's got a light-brown fringe that flutters just above his right eye. His eyes are always half-closed because, he thinks, it makes him look like a film star or something. But his ma, Auntie Gladys, says he shuts his eyes whenever he sees the alphabet.

On this hot December morning, Marlon and I are watching his ma in her garden pouring used tea leaves onto her rose bushes.

'Does it make them grow nice, Auntie Gladys?'

'Oh yes, they love the tea. Look at them.'

I believe Auntie Gladys because the yellow roses are a bright yellow and the red ones are as red as blood. But I'm not so sure about what Marlon is about to tell me. He takes an envelope out of the letterbox, opens it and removes a Christmas card. He looks at it and clicks his tongue in disgust.

This is not in the spirit of Christmas so I ask, 'What's wrong?'

'Look at that?' he says, shoving the card under my nose.

Jolly old Santa and his reindeer are racing through the snow. On top of the card brightly coloured letters say: 'HAPPY XMAS'.

I don't know what's wrong and I frown.

'Can't you see?' Marlon says.

'See what?'

'Read that.' He points to 'Happy Xmas'.

'Happy Christmas…'

'It doesn't say that, it say: Happy *Ex*mas.'

'Ja, but…'

'You see what they've done, Christopher, they've gone and crossed –' he makes a big X in the air with his index finger – 'Christ out of Christmas.'

I look at Marlon, I look across the tiny garden to see if Auntie Gladys agrees with her son. She's puffing away at a cigarette and loosening the soil around her rose bushes with a tiny spade. She blows smoke out and says:

'Marlon should know what he's talking about because when it comes to Xs his teachers are always putting them all over his books and his school reports.'

EVERYBODY GETS CHRISTMAS cards.

We get a card from the Crowders and it's not the X that makes me wonder, it's something else. The card reads:

To Nick, Shirley and Fam.
Happy Xmas and a prosperous New Year
From Jimmy, Noleen and Fam.

The card has come via the post office and there's a two-and-a-half cent stamp on the envelope to prove it. The funny thing is: the Crowders live right across the road from us. They could've walked over to our letterbox and just thrown the card in.

But I understand why they chose to post it: because it's official and it's grand and because it's Christmas.

SHAUNE AND ALISON sit in the lounge and count our Christmas cards. One day there's five. The next day there's nine; then suddenly there's fifteen. And it seems every time we go to the letterbox there's three or four more.

My brother and sister loop a long piece of string from one end of the lounge wall to the other, sticking the ends down with sticky tape. They hang all the cards on the string and step back to admire their handiwork: snow-covered hills blend into wise men gazing up at the stars, melt into lighted candles and baby Jesus in his crib, his mother Mary gazing tenderly at him.

'Is it nice, Ma?' Alison asks.

'Very nice,' Ma says. 'You could become an interior decorator.'

Alison claps her hands gleefully at the two big words she could become.

Everybody's getting new stuff. An OK Bazaars truck pulls up next door and delivers a new hi-fi to the Conways.

Another truck stops down the road at the Fishers and brings a new bedroom suite, shiny brown wardrobes, a matching brown headboard and a dressing table with a mirror that reflects us, pulling faces, and almost the whole of dirty, dusty Flinders Street.

It's two days to go to Christmas, two long days before we can wear our new clothes.

Ma stands on our stoep and calls me from the street where I'm playing football with Toolbag, Rathead, Vino and Conos and them.

'Yes, Ma?'

She gestures for me to come to her. It can only mean 'the shop', I tell myself as I trot into the yard, stand at the bottom of the stoep and look up at her.

'I want you to go to the shop. I need condensed milk, bread and cigarettes.'

I go. And twenty minutes later I'm back in the street. I'm about to score a goal when…

'Christopher!' It's Ma again.

On my way to the stoep I pass Toolbag who whispers, in a poor impersonation of Ma: 'You forgot the cheese, Chris my boy.' The boys laugh, but I'm in no mood for jokes.

Ma is becoming a real nuisance if you ask me. And that's the one problem I have with Christmas: the factories are closed, all the mothers are at home and you can't play a full game of football without a mother calling you: 'Sweep the yard, go to the shop, go and ask Auntie Mavis for some bicarb for my heartburn…'

Mothers complain because this time of the year all the fathers sneak out of the house early and head straight for the shebeen. And stay there the whole day. But can you blame them?

I go into our yard, walk up the path and look up at her standing in the doorway. I decide that this time I'm taking no nonsense – I'm no longer that little boy with the GOODYEAR/ Merc who used to race to the shops at eighty miles per hour.

'You forgot to buy the tomatoes,' Ma says, but she can't keep a straight face.

'Ma, you never told me to buy tomatoes!'

'OK, maybe I didn't but I need them now.'

'But Ma!' I stamp one foot into the dust. 'I've just been to the shops. Where's Derek? Why can't he go for a change!'

Ma gives one of those impatient sighs of hers. She rests on her other foot, looks me straight in the eye and says:

'Do you want me to take those Christmas clothes back to the shops?'

When next I open my mouth to speak, it is to say to the shopkeeper, 'Fifteen cents tomatoes please.'

But mostly Ma's nice. In the evenings, before Christmas, she plays rummy with me and Derek. She keeps the score with a pen and a foolscap page. Her handwriting is neat and her columns are straight and she adds and subtracts quickly – you won't say she dropped out of school in Standard Six.

We stay up until past eleven o'clock, playing cards and listening to LM Radio – but softly so that we don't wake up the others.

And then we make tea and Ma fetches scones that she baked that afternoon, or sweets that she hid away specially for tonight.

AND FINALLY IT'S Christmas. It's no longer around the corner, it is here! The first signs, when I get up, are the church bells ringing all over – the EBC Church close by in Colorado Drive, the Anglican Church in Asum Street, the Catholic Church in Cherwora Place – ding dong, ding dong.

The only ding dong we don't hear is from our own church, the Ebenezer – it's the furthest away, up there in Zone 2. And, according to Ma, my brothers and I have to be there in forty-five minutes' time.

There are crackles and squeaks in the bedroom as me, Shaune and Derek wriggle into new shirts, shoes and pants. Shaune gets more and more grumpy with every new item he puts on, from socks to silver-grey flannel shorts to royal-blue blazer.

'What's wrong?' Ma asks, straightening his bowtie.

'Why does our church have to be the farest away?'

'Furthest,' Derek corrects him.

Ma takes a deep breath as she thinks of something. 'Do you know how far those three wise men had to travel when they went to see Jesus?'

Shaune says, 'No, how far?'

'A thousand miles, all the way through the desert.'

'Which desert?' Derek wants to know.

'The Kalahari,' Ma says. But I know she's lying because for the quickest of moments she and Dad exchange looks and she tries to hide a mischievous smile. 'You guys have thirty-five minutes.'

Shaune is still not happy. 'That preacher is gonna talk for a long time!'

'I know,' Ma says, 'I asked him to.'

'Why?' Shaune says.

'So that I can finish the cooking. Right, move it.'

In church we hear the same sermon that we heard last year and the year before – Mary and Joseph couldn't find a place at the Inn, Jesus was born in a stable, the wise men came to visit the newborn baby…blah blah blah for over an hour.

On our way back, we pop in at the Jansens to wish them. And also at the Myburghs.

When we get home Ma has laid the table and it's time for Christmas lunch. There's so much chicken that almost everyone can have a drumstick. Alison doesn't mind not having one because Ma gives her a wing and says it's better than a drumstick.

'Why, Mommy?'

'With a drumstick you can only walk, but with a wing you can fly.'

And there's crispy roast potatoes and breyani with sour milk and grated carrot salad with onion and bits of dhunia in it.

The sad thing is that me and Derek and Shaune don't eat up all our food because when we popped in to wish the neighbours they gave us biscuits and gingerbeer.

'I distinctly told yous not to go spoiling your appetites,' Ma says. 'Did you hear me telling these children, Nick?'

But Dad is not listening. He's smiling because he's had his third brandy for the day. He was also told, I remember, not to touch that stuff until after lunch. So maybe Ma should say to me, 'Did you hear me telling your father, Chris?' But on Christmas day, it seems, nobody listens to Ma.

So even though the Christmas lunch is our biggest meal in twelve months, it's the one we hardly eat.

But we do eat the Christmas pudding with warm custard – because there are five-cent coins hidden in it! You chew and chew and – gaa – suddenly you bite onto this hard thing and you know you're five cents richer.

After lunch Derek and I go in search of Crowbar and Rathead and Hippie and whoever else wants to come along with us. We spend the afternoon going from door to door wishing all the neighbours.

'Happy Christmas, Mrs Wills.'

'And the same to you, my son. Oh shame, all the boys, looking so nice today!' (She says 'shame' whether something is good or bad.)

Next we go and wish Auntie Kathy and Uncle Danny who live just behind us in Colorado Drive. They're sitting with a young couple.

'Happy Christmas, Uncle Dan.'

Uncle Dan is so jolly he could be mistaken for Father Christmas's much slimmer brother. His glass is nicely filled with brandy and Coke and he's full of smiles and jokes.

He blows out a stream of smoke that makes the trimmings on the ceiling flutter. He turns to my brother and says, mock seriously, 'Hey my laaitie, where did you get these kwaai clothes?'

'My mother bought it, Uncle Dan.'

'Tell me, where does your father work again?'

'Anderson's Furniture.'

'Well tell him to get me a job there man, so that I can also buy myself a nice suit.'

Uncle Dan offers us the fare on the table: sweets, peanuts, raisins, mixed nuts, dainty fruit…I help myself to a couple of Quality Street chocolates.

'What about some peanuts?' Auntie Kathy says.

'No thank you.' I shake my head.

'Why not?' Auntie Kathy wants to know.

'There's too many peanuts in Riverlea today; everybody's got peanuts – everybody.'

Uncle Dan and his guests laugh so much that they almost spill their drinks. And for the first time I turn my attention to the couple. They're sitting side by side on the couch and they keep saying 'yorl' instead of 'yous'. It turns out they're from faraway Durban, relatives of Uncle Dan, spending the Christmas holidays in Joburg.

The woman, I see, is a very nice lady. And I don't mean nice like fat Mrs Wills who's forever asking us if we passed our exams. This woman has kicked off her sandals and she has her bare feet right on top of the couch. She's wearing a short summer dress. And every time she says 'yorl' it looks like she's getting ready for a kiss. Her eyes are big and shiny and the same colour as the brandy and Coke that she's sipping from a long glass.

'Yorl are all looking very larnie,' she says, bobbing up and down on the couch.

All five of us form a queue to wish her – handshake and a kiss, handshake and a kiss, handshake and a kiss. It's Crowbar's turn and then mine. And before I've even smacked my lips, it's over! I get an idea. I decide to get back in the queue and kiss her again. She's surely too tipsy to know that I've wished her already. And there's too many things happening in the room – my friends are laughing, Auntie Kathy's passing a bowl of sweets around, Uncle Dan is praising Conos's new shoes, music on the turntable – everything is too deurmekaar.

I get back in the queue. Handshake and…She looks up and says: 'Hah! You want another one – no problem.'

'No … I …' But the next thing I'm getting my second kiss – even better than the first one.

BACK IN THE street, the boys can't wait to compliment me.

'Does this man have guts or what?' Crowbar says, flinging an arm around my shoulder.

'What you mean?' But I know what he's talking about.

The others agree, and they're all full of praise for me.

'And in front of the boyfriend!'

'Gents, gents, gents,' I stop them before we move on to the next house. They form a little semicircle around me. I make a mock serious face before I tell them: 'I've got strong feelings for that lady.'

They all slap their thighs with laughter and give me high fives.

CHRISTMAS COMES TO an end in stages. First the trimmings come down, then someone eats the last biscuit in the tin, then mothers and fathers go back to work. And suddenly it's the first day of school. Ma divides the Christmas cards between me and Derek – each one gets a Father Christmas, wise men looking up at the bright star, and baby Jesus in his crib among the straw and the lambs. We cover our schoolbooks in brown paper and paste these pictures on the covers.

A week later, Ma brings home the brand new Adams catalogue! And this year, Ma says, she's definitely going to try for 'that 32-piece dinner serve us. Come hell or high water.'

Featuring China and
the thirty blikskottels

The movies. We call it bio – which is short for bioscope. Twenty-five cents for a double feature.

Hippie Johnson sees the two advertising posters in the window at the café and says: 'Hey, gents a double future.'

Conos and Vino and them laugh at him. He sticksed me for movies last week, so I try not to laugh. I'll have a good laugh later – in the double future – but right now I correct him.

There are no movie houses in Riverlea. Mostly they're in the city and for whites. But the Rayners' home in Derwent Street is where we watch our movies. Mr Rayners has a projector. Herman Rayners, who is in my class, says it's a sixteen millimetre. 'The same size that the white people have,' he says.

Actually I don't care if it's a fifty millimetre or twenty centimetre as long as it shows us movies every Saturday afternoon.

Herman is one of the coolest guys in Riverlea. He doesn't have to battle for attention like the rest of us, lying and bragging all over the place: 'My oupa killed three hundred Germans in the war'; 'My uncle could've married a white woman'; 'My father's got six pistols hidden away in the house but he told us to tell nobody'.

Herman doesn't have to talk such rubbish. In fact, Herman doesn't talk much. In fact, Herman doesn't even speak well, he mumbles. Herman gets the lowest marks for English recitation and Afrikaans recitation. Reciting isn't easy. You have to stand up in front and face the whole class. When Herman recites the Afrikaans poem about a boy who's scared to get up in the middle of the night to get a drink of water because there's a spook in the passage, and the English poem about the man who gets so happy when he sees a field of golden daffodils, it sounds exactly the same.

But on Friday afternoons during break, he becomes the most articulate and popular boy on the school grounds because he has information that we all desire. We form about three circles around him.

'Herman, tell us-tell us, what's your toppie showing tomorrow?'

'Th Mnifcent Svn.'

'Eish!'

'Herman isn't your dad showing a double feature?'

Herman nods and smiles.

'What's the second one called?'

Herman mutters the second one so softly that only those in the inner circle hear. This causes a commotion as some of us shout 'what-what?' and others 'eish!'.

None of us has seen these movies yet, but the titles alone are enough to get us jumping about.

The Rayners' house is exactly the same size and shape as everyone else's. This means their lounge is big enough for a family of four or five to sit comfortably. But on Saturdays it is transformed like magic. Out go the bulky couch and armchairs and lounge table. And in come a white sheet which is pinned on to the wall, and about thirty plastic and kitchen chairs and one or two wooden benches. We fill them up, me and Derek and Vino and Conos and Hippie and about twenty-five other excited neighbourhood boys and girls.

At about two o'clock (or an hour later if the sixteen millimetre's giving trouble) someone turns out the lights and we hear that all-too-familiar growl – grrrrrrrr. This gets our thirty hearts pumping – even though the growl is merely the sound of the projector and not the Metro Goldwyn Mayer lion.

33

For some reason this is a sign to start chatting excitedly to the person sitting next to you. Then, on to the screen numbers are flashed that count down from ten to zero, and of course we all break into a chorus of: 'Ten! Nine! Eight! Seven…!' By the time the movie starts there is so much shouting and screaming that it might as well be one of those silent movies.

Mr Rayners, like his son Herman, is not a man given to shouting loudly in public or in his own home. But he has to keep order somehow, so he has hired a big boy, one China Marais, a high school drop-out, who's got a talent for insulting and threatening other mothers' children.

The lights go on again and instead of the Wild West in technicolor we have China cursing.

'Bushmen,' he bellows louder than the jungle cry of Tarzan of the Apes, 'do yous wanna watch the movie or make a noise?'

Shouts of, 'It's him!' and 'It's not me!' go up, creating a completely new noise.

'Shut up you blikskottels!'

Silence.

'Listen,' says China. 'Nobody say nothing. Just shut up and listen.'

'OK, China.' The voice comes from the corner where Dannyboy Aspeling and his gang are sitting and throwing peanuts at us in the dark.

China looks over our heads and says, 'Aspeling you think I don't know it's you. If you wanna be clever just tell me. If you don't watch your step I'll give you your twenty-five cents back and you won't put your scurvy feet in this bioscope again.'

Eventually China gets about ninety-nine per cent silence, which is good enough, and the lights go out again.

Grrrrr.

We spent more time trying to watch the movies than Cecil B. DeMille and them spend making them.

The Red Indians, their angry faces streaked with war paint, creep up on the lone cowboy, the ouchie we call him, drinking water from the stream. Thirty hearts stop beating and we all shout: 'Arra, ouchie!' This time China leaves us to scream – in fact, he's doing a bit of shouting himself.

But we have nothing to worry about. Our man in the hat and boots spotted the danger long before we did and – *bangbangbang* – three Red Indians lie dead in the grass, the feathers in their hair fluttering in the breeze.

In Africa Tarzan has to survive similar dangers. A bunch of half-naked natives armed with spears crouch in a bush ready to impale the lord of the apes.

'Tarzan, watch out behind you!' we all shout.

But we don't have to stress. A bunch of chattering monkeys in a tree warn the king of the jungle. With his famous scream – *aheeeyaaheeyaa* – he swings into action and sends the natives scattering in all directions.

It doesn't take much to get us clapping or stomping: for a fight in a saloon in which the ouchie beats up about five bandits single-handedly. In the process they also smash up the whole saloon: glasses, bottles, tables and chairs, pillars that keep up the roof, everything, but nobody offers to pay for the damage; a showdown where the ouchie shoots dead twenty Apaches with one six-shooter – without reloading once; Zorro fluttering like a giant bat in his black cape on the roof of a hacienda to rescue a pretty senorita. Or just the animated antics of Donald Duck, Mickey Mouse and Bugs Bunny.

For days after watching a Western, we're all calling each other 'muchacho' and using words like 'aint' and 'crittur'.

The end.

Scrap heap

When we leave for school in the mornings, our parents are forever saying, 'And come straight home.' But nobody in their right mind ever goes straight home.

What awaits you at home? Bread and jam and homework.

But between school and home there are hundreds of pleasures and treasures that can almost make you forget where you live. Take for instance the mineholes in the veld just beyond the school fence. They are deep and dangerous and if you fell into one of those it could take the fire brigade ten hours to get you out – if you survive the fall in the first place.

There's Widas, the old Jewish shop that served the miners many years ago and is still doing business. The rich boys buy chips and Coke there, the rest of us buy sherbert.

There's the gola pipes. Some afternoons you might want to disappear for a while from the face of the Earth. You climb down into a stormwater drain in Colorado Drive and, like magic, you surface again half a kilometre away near the railway line!

And then there's the scrap heap. The scrap heap is not a permanent feature, like the gola pipes or the mineholes. The scrap heap is here today, gone tomorrow. It's like a circus that comes into town for a while, for a moment of magic and entertainment. And when you blink ... it's gone.

On the northern side of Riverlea is Industria with all its factories – a jam factory, a sweet factory, furniture and cigarette factories. This is where many of our parents and older brothers and sisters work.

The factories are close enough for the workers to walk to work every morning, crossing a stretch of veld.

It is through this stretch of veld that we walk home from school. And it is here that the factories dump their unwanted rubbish, their scrap.

You go to school in the morning, walking through the veld, along paths, underneath gum trees, through long grass. Six hours later, you and your schoolmates are slouching through that same veld on your way home. And suddenly, what do you see ahead of you: a mountain as huge as a classroom and almost as high. Where this morning there was nothing there is now rubbish for all!

And that's how I got into trouble one day.

It's January. I'm in Standard Two and Mr Alexander is our new teacher. He seems strict this one, growling and threatening us all the time: 'Just try me'; 'Ask the Standard Threes about me'; 'I already know who the troublemakers are among you'.

He's in his twenties but he's already lost all his hair and maybe that's what's making him cross. He introduces his cane to us. 'Meet Gerty,' he says, swishing it in the air. 'She's brand new. I fetched her from the blind school last week.'

The school for the blind is four kilometres away, in Coronationville where my granny lives. On the way to my granny's we – cousins and uncles – always stop to watch through a window, blind men and women making wicker baskets, chairs and tables from long strips of cane.

Well, Gerty should've been part of a white family's patio furniture in a holiday flat down there in Durban or Cape Town. But instead, Gerty will be spending her days at T.C. Esterhuysen Primary School, stinging the bums of the Standard Twos.

I decide on a plan for the year. I'm going to try to make myself invisible in this class. Put up my hand whenever I know the answer to a question, pretend I'm thinking hard for those questions I don't know, and for the rest of the time just shut up.

But my plan doesn't work. The next morning I become the first victim of Gerty. And I become bad friends with a fellow classmate Abel Applegryn.

This is a sad story and it goes like this.

Abel Applegryn is a new friend. He hasn't got other friends. The reason is because he smells a bit. The boys, Rowan and Kurt and Tommy and them, all call him Stinky. And, sadly, they're right; there is a nasty smell wherever Abel goes. In class Mr Alexander sniffs the air and tells the big boys to open the windows.

'They are open, sir,' they say.

'Well just open some more!'

With a long pole they open even the very high ones but the smell doesn't go away.

Abel's teeth are yellow.

'When Abel smiles you can see he's a Chelsea supporter,' the boys say. Chelsea's colours are black shorts and yellow top.

Don't even talk about the earjam in his ears!

One afternoon after school, we're all making our way home. Everyone is walking with somebody; there's groups of three, five, four, even six. But Abel is walking alone kicking stones. I break away from my group of Rathead, Toolbag and Hippie and I go and walk with Abel.

Immediately I get the smell but all you have to do when your friend has a smell is just walk on the other side. And that's what I do.

So Abel and I become walk-home – and even playground – chommies. One day we're walking home from school and we hear the shouts of the boys up ahead of us. And we both know what it means.

'Scrap heap!' we both shout out loud. And we join the race towards the veld.

The trucks have been busy while we were learning. There are about six heaps and already there are kids around and on top of each one of them.

Abel and I reach the heaps and we start to forage – which we call digging.

When we're digging everybody forgets about Abel's stinky smell. I reckon it's because the smell here is so strong that it overpowers Abel's odour. Even Abel, before he gets stuck in, turns up his nose and says, 'Sies!'

You meet a lot of friends on the heaps. Actually, you don't really meet them, you just hear their familiar voices, scratching about and throwing things aside.

The only time you look up is when someone says 'Eish!' That means they've found something grand.

Abel gets lucky: after hardly a minute of looking he finds an empty Beechies box, Musk. Well, its last owner thought it was empty and threw it away. But Abel shakes it and it makes that last-one-in the-box noise.

He bites off one half and gives the other half to me.

Diana van Rensburg gives a shout. We look up: she's holding up a smart beige lady's handbag. The lining is tattered, but all you do is rip out all the lining and you can still put stuff in there.

It's Diana's lucky week: a few days ago she won a packet of chocolates – second prize in a school raffle. She slings the bag over her shoulder and pretends to be one of those fancy rich white women we see in the restaurants in town.

'Oh, I got to be going now,' she says, blowing imaginary cigarette smoke into the air, 'the chauffeur is waiting.'

We laugh, but not for long because we're eager to find our own treasure.

Crowbar is on the very top of a heap. He looks into the distance and sees something. 'Guess who's coming,' he says, skipping down like Billy Goat Gruff and making clouds of dust with each step.

'Who?'

'The Yellow Vipers. Flea and them.'

Everybody on the heap, including me, utters their favourite swear word. What do we do, run away because we're scared of them, or stay to make them believe we're not really afraid. While we're all trying to decide, they suddenly appear, like three cockroaches come to claim their share of rubbish.

'Hey, hey, hey!' they shout, to announce that they're here to take over proceedings.

'Flea and them' are three Standard Five boys who live across the railway line in Zombie Town. Dik Toon (Big Toe) is the biggest amongst them – he should've been in high school a year or two ago already. He goes around barefoot winter and summer. He walks on hot tar, sharp stones, through thornbushes – no problem. The only thing that hurts his feet are shoes. Last year his teacher Mrs Brown said, 'Shame, poor Patrick!' and went and bought him a pair of brand new Bata Toughees out of her own pocket. He wore them for a week and then gave them to his uncle.

If you're playing marbles in the street and you see Dik Toon coming, grab your marbles and run. Because after Dik Toon has walked by, your marbles are gone – stuck between his toes!

Even though he's still in primary school, Dik Toon plays left back for the Young Lions under twenties. These boys all have football boots but they accuse Dik Toon of dirty play and kicking them.

Then there's Barretta. He's the only boy in Riverlea who got caned by the police at Langlaagte police station three times in one year. The last time they flogged him, it was because they caught him red-handed in Thorn Lighting stealing light bulbs.

The police asked him why he had stolen light bulbs if he doesn't have electricity at home. His answer was that he was going to sell the light bulbs and buy candles.

And there's Flea. He's the boss of the Yellow Vipers despite his tiny body – and squeaky voice. Big bulging eyes, like a chameleon, and thick lips that stay scurvy all year round. His gums and tongue are bright red and his teeth are big. Crowbar says he swallowed a red velvet lounge suite.

'Heita, Flea!' we all greet him eagerly, even waving.

Flea says, 'Ja, my laaities.' It means, 'Hi, kids.' We all feel proud that Flea responded to our greeting.

The Vipers are in a good mood today. There will be no bullying from them, no slapping anybody or cursing someone's mother. They start digging for stuff and we all breathe a sigh of relief into the rotten air.

In the meantime, Derek has also arrived on the scene. In no time he pulls out a small box. It's heavy and closed and looks new, despite the ash and dirt on it.

'Bosch Spark Plugs,' Derek reads hesitantly but getting all three words right. He beams, as if Mrs Keston has pasted a gold star in his book.

'Not bad,' says Flea. 'Dig some more, you might find a car for those.'

We all laugh, even Derek.

But unfortunately there are old spark plugs in the new box.

We go on foraging until Crowbar screams out a triumphant: 'Yes!' and, 'Anybody got a match?'

We look up and he's relaxing on his bum with a brand new cigarette between his lips, looking for all the world as if he's never tasted his Ma's belt. He's found a packet of Rothmans twenties with at least four cigarettes in it.

Flea gives him the curling finger and Crowbar meekly hands over the cigarettes.

'You're too young to smoke, my laaitie,' Flea tells him. We watch the Yellow Vipers boss light up and puff away expertly until, with a wave of a small hand, Flea tells us all to 'Scratch. Stop staring at me as if I'm John Wayne.'

A Standard One boy, scratching near me, finds a colouring-in book with most of the pictures still left un-coloured.

'Now you have to look for crayons,' I joke.

But the biggest find of the day is a small pocket radio, complete with batteries in it, which works! Found by Dik Toon himself.

I am envious. I would love a pocket radio to listen to late shows on Springbok Radio, like *The World of Hammond Innes*, in bed when I should be sleeping.

Flea finds a long rope. He's pleased. He announces to us all that he will be using it to tie up Mr Goliath, his teacher.

'Look out for us at break tomorrow,' he says, 'when I will be dragging him around the school grounds like a puppy.'

There's something that almost everybody gets but which nobody wants – except me: magazines, comics and books.

Every now and then I hear somebody say, 'Give that to Chris'; 'Here's another one for Chris'; 'It's only a book, give it to Chris'. And so the magazines, comics and books pile up by my side – *See*, a weekly photocomic of love stories. There's a lot of kissing in it, and pretty girls who are always saying, 'Oh, darling!' Sometimes there are two men in love with the same girl and then she has to choose one.

But this *See* smells a little and the last page is missing. It ends where these two guys are driving along a road and one says to the other: 'But what if she's not there?'

It's irritating when the ending is torn off, but I'll read it anyway. And then I'll just make up the end myself.

I also get a *Spooky* and a *Captain Hurricane*. The only problem with them are dog ears. But that's not serious. I slap them against my leg to get the dust out, and put them on my pile.

At one point somebody nudges me. I look up, it's Flea. He's holding out a *Captain Devil* photocomic. 'Take, sonny,' he says.

'Thanks, Flea.' I don't believe it; even Flea knows what to do with a good book.

Two or three hours later, the rubbish dump is almost flattened and quiet and we've all gone home with our booty. It's the turn of the doves and the sparrows now, who come to see if there's something for them too – maybe an ostrich feather or a piece of rag to line their nest.

I spend the rest of the afternoon reading my smelly comics. I've forgotten all about school and Mr Alexander and the fearsome Gerty. But tomorrow morning I'll be reintroduced to all three of them in an unforgettable way.

The next day we all get to Mr Alexander's class on time. (He warned us that Gerty hates latecomers and was eager to show us what would happen to anyone who came even a minute after the bell.) We start with the Lord's Prayer: 'Our father, which art in heaven, yellow bee thy name…'

'Take out your new Maths textbooks,' says Mr Alexander. 'And turn to page sixteen.'

Click-click-click, go the locks on the school bags, including mine. And plop-plop-plop go the books landing on the desks – except mine.

My heart starts beating loud in my chest, boom-boom-boom. What now? Did I leave it at home? Did I leave it at school? Did it fall out of my case on my way home yesterday? My mind is going from here to there to there, flipping all over the place like those balls in the pinball machine in Mr Adams's Takeaways.

Allan Sandberg is my desk neighbour. I whisper to him to move his book to the centre so that we can share it.

He knows I've got a problem, and he's a real pal, very discreetly sliding his book to the centre. I hope Mr Alexander won't see what's going on here. But his attention is somewhere else. Someone's hand is up. It's Abel.

'Yes!' Mr Alexander barks at him.

What's going on? We haven't even started the lesson yet and already Abel wants to know something.

Abel slides out of his seat with a textbook in his hand. He goes up to Mr Alexander. I can't hear what he's saying. But the next thing, Mr Alexander looks up at me!

'You come here, Van Wyk!' he barks at me.

I go up.

'Is this yours?' he asks, holding up my Maths textbook.

'Yes, sir.'

'So I give you a book, which, by the way, is the property of the Department of Coloured Affairs. I tell you to cover it, to put a nice picture on it, to learn from it. And what do you do? You go and chuck it on the rubbish dump!'

Before I can say anything, I'm bending over and Gerty's stinging my bum six times.

As I stumble back to my desk, someone whispers, 'How does Gerty taste?' followed by sniggering.

My bum is on fire and I'm humiliated. But most of all I'm angry. I can't believe that Abel betrayed me. The one nobody else wanted to be friends with but me. I know how this all came about: yesterday at the rubbish heaps, I had my Maths textbook in my hands. I put it aside so that I could scratch with both hands, but

I found things and Flea and his gang came, and Crowbar found cigarettes and Diana found a handbag, and in all that excitement I forgot all about the book. Abel picked it up. But instead of giving it back to me, he decided to bring it to Mr Alexander – and to Gerty.

He wants to get into the teacher's good books, but he doesn't mind selling out a friend. The other day I passed Mr Francis's classroom. The door was open and I saw something there that made me stop and watch for a second or two.

A boy called Hubert is about to get a hiding. But Hubert refuses to bend. Mr Francis calls four big boys to come and hold him down. Each one grabs hold of a limb and they bend him forward – and all four of them are Hubert's friends!

I quickly walked away from that open door before Mr Francis could turn around and invite me in for a taste of his cane too. A cane that probably also had a name.

But what I saw bothered me. Maybe, I told myself, it's not easy to say 'no' to a teacher when he asks you to hold down a boy for a flogging, even if that boy is your friend.

But with Abel it's a different story. He could simply have given me the book and Mr Alexander would never have known what happened.

From Standard One, if you stopped talking to a friend, what the two of you did was smash thumb against thumb. You were then officially 'bad friends'. But I was a big boy now and I didn't go in for that silly thumb ritual any more. But Abel knows we are no longer friends. During first break he comes up to me with a packet of peanuts and he says: 'Open your hand,' so that he can pour some in. I just shove his hand away and walk away.

Second break he tries again. I go to the tap to drink some water. He's there before me and he leaves the tap open so that I don't have to open it myself. I close the tap, open it and drink.

After school I walk home with Allan Sandberg and Hippie Johnson and them.

'That Abel laaitie's a dog,' Allan says.

We all nod in agreement.

'I wonder what ou Alexander promised him?' Hippie says.

'Maybe a can of deodorant,' I joke.

'What you talking about deodorant?' says Allan. 'I think a can of Doom.'

Abel and I remained bad friends for a long time (about two weeks). I actually planned to be bad friends with him for ever and ever but then he made another move.

One afternoon there's a knock at our front door. I open it.

It's Abel. He's standing on the stoep. He's not looking up at me like he's supposed to; his head is buried in the pages of his dog-eared, fatty, blotchy, inky English exercise book. He's muttering verbs and adjectives and stuff, trying to pretend that he doesn't know I'm in the doorway and that we've never had a fight.

'What you want?'

Only then does he look up, jerking his head back as if he's surprised to see me.

'Eish, this stuff here, I can't work it out,' he says. 'Can you show me how to do it?'

I'm not the only one in the class who can do this English homework. There's Lorna Williams and Cliffie Mills. Abel's walked right past both their homes to get here. I let him in because you can't chase a man away from your door. He still smells and I leave the door open for a bit of a breeze to blow in.

We're going to have an English grammar exam and he's having trouble with comparisons. He shows me what he's done so far. His work is so bad, I suspect he might have messed it up deliberately just to make me laugh. It goes:

Pretty	*Prettier*	*The prettiest*
Clean	*Dry clean*	*Dirty again*
Swim	*Swimmer*	*The swimmest*
Sweet	*Sweeter*	*The sweetest*
Tough	*Toffee*	*Toffee*

'You got two right.' I show him which ones.

'What about "swim"?'

'That's not even an adjective,' I explain to him. 'It only works with adjectives; "swim" is a verb.'

About an hour later he's getting almost all right. He thanks me and when he's ready to leave, he says, 'I'm sorry I took your book to Mr Alexander.'

I nod.

'Can we play together again?'

I know my answer but I make as if I'm thinking hard about it for a while. Then I nod.

TWO DAYS LATER, after our exam, Abel comes over to my house again.

'I got good news and bad news,' he says.

'What's the bad news?'

'My father died this morning.'

'You lie!'

But, even though he doesn't really look sad, I can see that he's not lying – maybe because people don't lie about such things, or because of the way he bites his lip with his yellow teeth.

'I'm sorry, Abel. Accept my deepest sympathy.'

He nods, and says, 'You wanna hear the good news?'

'What's the good news?'

'I passed.'

Going to Japan

I take out my clothes and stuff:

two shirts, one blue, one yellow
two boxer shorts, one black, one blue
two T-shirts, one white, one blue
two Elmar underpants, both white, one slightly broken in
front
my old Bata Toughees shoes
a pair of socks
one dark brown V-neck jersey (it's summer but Ma said, 'Take
it with – you never know')
my toothbrush

I don't have a hanky. (I don't remember ever seeing a boy with a hanky in those days.) I take out my Spypen which I bought at Roys for Toys in town. It's like binoculars but you clip it into your top pocket and your friends think it's a pen. You can stand in a secret spot and watch people from a distance without them realising you're watching them.

I would like to take it with me, but I decide not to. Where I'm going there are lots of wild cousins and I can't see my pen coming back home in one piece. I'll just tell them about the pen and say that I forgot to bring it. I take one last look through it before I put it away – I aim it at the Edwards' yard. No one's about. There's a coalbox, a woodbox, a bicycle frame nailed to the wall. There's a dishcloth fluttering on the washline, a few clothespegs relaxing upside down because they have nothing to do. Sticking out of the dustbin I can see a soap powder box that says 'Surf with Superb'. It actually says 'Superblue' but the 'lue' is in the bin and this is a Spypen, not an X-ray pen. How boring. This is why I'm leaving Riverlea for a week.

I also take:

my hardcover *Tintin* comic that my uncle Mellvin gave me
my hardcover *Hardy Boys* novel that my ouma bought me at
   a secondhand bookshop
three *True Africa* photocomic books

True Africa is all about Samson, a black crime-fighter who lives in a jungle and fights crime. If you think that the villages are peaceful and crime free, think again. Samson uncovers all kinds of evil plots and brings bad guys to justice.

I love the adventures of Samson but there's something that irritates me about these comics: at the end of every right-hand page it says: 'PLEASE TURN OVER' or 'CONTINUED OVERLEAF'. It's as if I'm going to read to the end of page three, not realise that I have to turn the page, and say, 'Oh I wish I knew what happens next! How can I find out?'

I take two *Spiderman* and two *Superman* comics that I haven't read yet. And a *Sad Sack* and a *Boris Karloff* which I've read about three times each.

Sad Sack is a useless guy and there's nothing he does right. If he walks into a house he trips. He picks up a cup of coffee and it falls right out of his hands. Ask him to paint a wall and he'll somehow end up painting his own face instead. Sad Sack is clumsy, but his stupidity makes you laugh.

Whenever me or Derek or Shaune do something stupid, Ma says, 'Sad Sack.'

Boris Karloff is not funny at all. His stories are full of ghosts and cemeteries and coffins and stuff. The Boris Karloff stories always begin with him in the first frame of the comic introducing you to his next tale of 'life' in the 'Twilight Zone'. He'll say something like this:

In 1811 the Count and Countess Baarhoffer lived in a castle in Germany. One sad night Lady Baarhoffer died after suffering from consumption. On the day of her funeral her coffin disappeared – never to be found – until, one hundred years later on the anniversary of her death…

And so begins a chilling tale full of corpses and lanterns and men in capes and bats flapping about in the dark.

I take all this stuff – my clothes and my comics – and put it in an OK Bazaars carrier bag – except the old shoes because I'm already wearing them.

I sit on the bed and wait for my uncle Mellvin to come and fetch me. There's still a week left before school opens and, just like every year, I'm going to spend it at my ouma's home in Coronation. All my uncles and cousins are there and they know how to have fun in the holidays.

My ouma is like the old woman

who lived in a shoe
She had so many children
She didn't know what to do.
She gave them some broth
Without any bread

My ouma lives in a shoe shaped like a house. She has eleven children and Ma is one of them. Half are married and the other half are still at home. (And I hope one of them is on his way here to fetch me right now.)

My favourite cousin Richard also lives there most of the time.

My ouma is sort of on the poor side, but she doesn't give us broth for supper. (I don't even know what broth is.) Mostly we get pap and wors, or pilchards with bread. Or she buys cheap tinned food from a neighbour who works at Koo, the canning factory in Industria. These tins are cheap because the labels have come off before they could leave the factory and now nobody knows what's inside – baked beans, peas, sweetcorn; it could be anything.

When Ouma's about to open the tins, we sit around the table and guess. Sometimes it's things we never even knew existed, but which white people eat, like olives!

My ouma has a bottle of fat in her fridge. It's the leftover oil from the liver and wors that she fries. If we're hungry and there's no peanut butter or jam for the bread, Ouma spreads some fat on. It's delicious, but there's one problem: the fat sometimes sticks to your palate and makes you talk funny.

The Afrikaans name for palate is 'verhemelte'. And the Afrikaans word for heaven is 'hemel'. So when the fat sticks onto their palates my cousins say: 'I've got fat stuck to my for heaven's sake.'

They say lots of those kinds of things, know lots of songs, riddles and jokes, and that's why I always go to Corrie in the holidays.

MY MA'S AT work. By the time she gets home I'll be gone. She said goodbye to me last night. She also said:

'And when you come back home make sure you come with all your clothes.'

'But I always do.'

'Oh no, you don't. The last time you left half your stuff behind.'

All I left behind was a T-shirt that had more holes than T-shirt. Now I hear it was half my stuff. Some people don't know their fractions.

My ouma promised that Mellvin would fetch me, but what if she forgot to tell him? He did forget the last time. I waited and waited for nothing – like a fool. Then my ma comes from work that evening and sees me and says:

'What are you doing here?'

It's like it's not my home any more.

'Mellvin didn't fetch me.'

'Why not?'

'Aw, Ma, how should I know?' Nobody in Riverlea – or Corrie – has phones. And it's not as if he sent a telegram saying:

Could not fetch you. Urgent things to attend to.

My brothers and sister are not interested in my problems. They're kissing Ma and taking a peep in her bag to see if there's something for them. And there is: a Kit-Kat for each; the small, two-and-a-half cent one with the two strips.

'And me, Ma?'

'You're not supposed to be here,' she says with a chuckle. 'You're supposed to be in Coronation, remember?'

My three siblings know what's about to happen next and Shaune grabs his Kit-Kat and heads for the back door with some speed. But Ma calls him back.

'Each of you give Chris a strip,' Ma says.

Shaune's lips quiver as he does some quick arithmetic.

'What, no!' he cries out. 'Then he'll have three strips and we'll have one each.'

Alison says, with a sob, 'Chris is just greedy!'

Ma says, 'Hold it, just hold it. If you each give him half a strip all four of you will end up with a strip and a half.'

Alison says point-blank, 'No!' and she licks her Kit-Kat all over to show me and Ma that she means business.

My brothers give me half a strip each.

A few minutes later Ma's got the pots going on the stove. She calls me. 'Go to the shop for me quickly.'

'Ah, Ma! I'm supposed to be in Corrie, remember?'

'But you're here now,' Ma says.

I go, but I'm not too happy about it.

MY *TINTIN* BOOK is sticking out of the carrier bag. I take it out and start reading, even though I've read the story about five times before. Actually I'm not really reading the book, I'm just looking at the pictures of Tintin and his dog Snowy and the Thompson and Thomson twins.

I like comics. I like the fat exclamation mark when somebody gets a fright, and the bright light bulb in the speech bubble whenever somebody has a good idea.

When Ma told my siblings to each give me half a strip of Kit-Kat, a light bulb went on above Shaune's head when he worked out that I would end up with more than them. But my sister had a fat exclamation mark above her head because she was indignant.

'Hey, sonny!'

There's that exclamation mark in a bubble just above my head. I look up. It's Mellvin, standing in the doorway. He's smiling at me and frogs' legs spread out around his eyes.

'You daydreaming again! You thought I wasn't gonna fetch you, hey!'

'No, I knew you'd come.' I try to sound nonchalant.

'The traffic was heavy,' he says.

We both laugh because he actually walked all the way here and we're going to walk the six kilometres back to Coronation. But mostly I laugh because I'm happy.

MELLVIN AND I hit the road.

We walk through the veld on the outskirts of Riverlea past the minedump and old mineshafts.

From the moment my uncle comes to fetch me, I want to ask him about my cousin Richard. But even though I'm bursting to ask, I don't, and it's because I want to be cool.

I decided this after reading my *Spiderman* comics and watching Steve McQueen in *The Great Escape*. The one thing that these guys have in common is that they are cool. And that means that they don't get excited and start acting silly – like a certain boy who lives in Riverlea and is on his way to his granny.

If we're playing football and I want a team-mate to pass me the ball, I yell, together with eight or nine other guys: 'Me-me-me-me-me!' That is not cool.

If I know the answer to a question in class, my hand flies up and I join a chorus shouting: 'Ma'am-ma'am-ma'am-ma'am-ma'am!' That is the opposite of cool.

When one of the guys comes into the street with a big fat vetkoek stuffed with mince, I join the hordes with shouts of: 'Gee stuk, gee stuk!' That's not cool, it's greedy.

I'm going to turn over a new leaf. A cool leaf. But for now I can't contain my excitement for much longer. I turn to my uncle and ask him:

'Is Japan there?'

'Huh?'

'Is Japan there?'

'Japan? Well, if you take a look at a map, to the east of Africa ... '

'You know what I mean!' I stomp my foot.

'Be specific, my laaitie.'

'Well, is he there?'

'Jislaaik, look at that,' he points at nothing in particular.

'Mell-vin!'

'He's there, he's there. Don't get excited.'

Now I know, and I can be cool again.

'Does he know I'm coming?'

'Yes, he's waiting for you.'

Now I'm happy and I can go back to being cool. Japan is my favourite cousin, by far. He's only about ten months older than me, but sometimes I get the feeling that he's a whole two or three years older because he knows lots of things that you can't learn at school. He's been to an Indian wedding, he once slipped into the Lyric Cinema in Fordsburg without paying, he once went to buy cigarettes for Rafiq Khan, the biggest gangster in Fordsburg, who always says, according to Japan, 'Me, I pulled twenty years.'

WE CALL HIM Japan because he wants to be a karate champion.

His real name is Richard – or Rashaad. You see, his ma and dad got divorced. His pa, Uncle Willie, who is my ma's brother, remarried and went to live in Eldorado Park. Japan's ma, Auntie Badder, remarried and went to live in Fordsburg. For a few months Richard lives with his pa – and then he's Richard. He worships at the Anglican church where he kneels on a small cushion ten times during the service and says the Lord's Prayer. And when it's his turn to say grace at supper time he says: 'For what we are about to receive, Lord make us truly grateful for Christ's sake. Amen.'

Then, after a few months his ma fetches him to stay with her in Fordsburg and he becomes Rashaad again. Now it's off to mosque and he has to take off his shoes to show his respect for a holy place. And at supper time it's 'Biesmallah' – only that one word, and salaam alaikum instead of a plain hullo whenever he greets anyone.

This year, my granny decided that Japan should stay with her and he attends Corrie Primary.

After about twenty minutes my uncle and I are in Industria. It's full of furniture factories, a canning factory, railway sidings, shops that sell pap and tomato gravy to workers in blue overalls.

This is where my oupa used to work before he died, and where Uncle Eddie (Mellvin's older brother) now works.

There's a high steel bridge across a railway line. Actually it's a twin bridge; one side has a sign that says: 'Europeans Only/Net Blankes'. The other one says: 'Non-Whites/Nie-Blankes'. We know which one is for us. As we walk across I wonder what's on the white bridge that's different to our side. To tell the truth, I've never seen a white person cross the bridge. There are thousands of black workers in Industria, and for every three hundred or so there is one white boss. And that boss doesn't come near this bridge; he just gets into his fancy car and goes home. So the bridge is nothing but a white elephant.

We walk for a while in silence, past the bottle store. And it reminds Mellvin about something.

'Did I tell you what happened in Coronation last week – about how some burglars robbed the bottle store?'

'Tell me-tell me!' (I'm forgetting to be cool.)

'The stupid idiots. Instead of carrying the booze out of the shop, they started drinking as much as they could right there.'

'And so?'

'The next morning the owner opens the shop. He sees this big mess and these three guys lying fast asleep on the floor.'

'And so?'

'He phones the cops and they come and kick the living daylights out of them and throw them into the kwela-kwela and take them to jail.'

'Jislaaik!'

Uncle Mellvin is in Standard Seven. He tells me about school. Last week their Afrikaans teacher, Mr de Beer, told them to prepare a five-minute speech on a topic of their choice.

Mellvin chose the moon landing, but he made his story funny and called it: 'Een klein stappie oppie maan, een groot stappie virrie manne'.

Not only is it funny, it's clever too. It sounds like an Afrikaans translation of Neil Armstrong's famous words when he set foot on the moon, but it's a whole confused thing.

'Where did you hear that?' I ask him after I've had a good chuckle.

'Made it up myself, sonny,' he says proudly.

An hour later we're a few blocks away from my ouma's house when one of my smaller cousins spots us. He runs into the house and comes out seconds later with uncles and cousins and Ouma herself wearing an apron. She puts one hand over her eyes like a visor and gazes down the road to see if she can see us.

'Haai, look who's here!' she says with a chuckle.

The kids around her! They're dancing and skipping and pointing and whistling. It's as if they've run from their street games that very second but can't stop their arms and legs from playing kennekie and gatjie klip and kirriebekke.

And if Ouma is Africa then Mellvin was right about Japan – he's standing to the east of her.

Japan and them come running to meet me, but Ouma stands behind chuckling some more.

'Ja Riverlea spy,' Neil says, giving me a friendly punch on the arm. This word 'spy' has got nothing to do with clues and secrets and disguises. If James Bond ever came to Corrie, on Her Majesty's Secret Service, he'd hear the word 'spy' so often he'd go mad. And then he'd fly straight back to London and tell his boss, 'Please, please, send me to Russia, I can only deal with one spy at a time.' To call someone a spy here is to say that he is of a lower species. 'Riverlea spy' means that not only me but all the people of Riverlea are not up to much.

'Ja, moegoe,' says my little uncle Doc. His name is Denzil but we call him Doc because he wants to be a doctor when he grows up. (If we knew how his life would turn out we would've called him Printer.)

Japan says, 'Howzit, sonny.' He takes a peep into my packet of clothes, dips a hand in and brings out one of my underpants. He sniffs at it and pretends to have a coughing fit. Everyone laughs, even my ouma, who slaps her palms together in delight.

Mellvin stands aside watching these antics, shaking his head as if in disapproval – but grinning all the while. He has delivered me, his job is done. And for most of my holiday I will hardly see him. He's fifteen and I hear he hangs around with his friends Vincent and Paul. They spend the whole day lying on the lounge carpet at Paul's mother's house, smoking and listening to Grand Funk Railroad, Uriah Heep and Deep Purple LPs and talking about nothing else but girls.

They all have long hair, especially during the holidays when there are no teachers around to cane you for looking like a 'hippie'. They also wear Levi jeans and the most colourful shirts I've ever seen.

Vincent came around to visit Mellvin one day with a shirt spattered with graffiti, printed in capital letters and cursive and small letters all mixed up! While they were by the gate chatting I stepped around Vincent – from right sleeve to left and from front to back – reading his shirt – and irritating Mellvin.

SocRaTEs eaTs hEMLOcK
FLOwER POWER
BAN THE BOMb
PeAce in oUr Time

'Socrates eats hemlock?' I said it over and over again. Who is Socrates and what is hemlock?

'Excuse me, Vincent?'

'Sonny,' Mellvin said, 'can't you see we're talking here?'

'It's cool, it's cool,' said Vincent. 'Let the kid ask his question.' He turned to me and flipped up his eyebrows rather coolly.

'Who is Socrates?'

He shrugged.

'And what's hemlock?'

He shrugged again. 'Can't help you there.'

So I walked away muttering, 'Socrates eats hemlock' for the rest of that day.

BUT THAT WAS in the past. Now I come to Ouma, who kisses me, wipes sweat off my nose and fiddles with my ears.

One-two-three and I'm in the street playing kirriebekke. This is where I want to be and back there in Riverlea my mother can come home this evening with big Kit-Kats for those spies Derek, Shaune and Alison because I don't care.

Kirriebekke is a team game. Sharon and Venecia, my two aunts, are the team leaders and they divide us into two teams of seven players each (neighbours have also come to play). It's sort of like cricket but played with a football: one team fields and the other goes 'in', kicking the ball and scoring runs until they're all thrown or caught out.

Our team goes in first and I score about thirty runs. My team cheers every time I kick that ball. And of course the opposition groans as they see defeat looming in Hamilton Street.

This is a miracle – in Riverlea the most I've ever scored is about fifteen runs in one game. With every kick, every run, I am convinced that I am becoming more athletic, more focused, a more strategic team player.

My ouma comes out of the house and looks over the fence. She applauds every time I score a run, but then she says:

'Look at the sweat on your face, boykie! Let me get you a hat.'

'No, Ma! I don't want no hat!' Ouma thinks I'm that rich boy Wilfred who lives three doors away from here and is forever wearing a silly hat. He calls his granny Oobie and she calls him Ducky. Sies!

During a break we all go to the backyard tap for a drink of water. Not only do I quench my thirst but I also splash some water on my head and I hope that everyone will think that it's sweat.

The next day things are not so good. We play football and I fail to score a goal. Actually I do score, but an own goal. These Coronation boys are just too fast for me. And don't talk about their tricks! I don't know how many times I try to kick the ball and end up kicking wind.

I really can't work out the difference between the miracle of yesterday and today's disaster. But give me about four or five years and I'll begin to understand: on the first day everyone was happy to see me and made everything go my way. Twenty-four hours later and I had become just another cousin, another nephew.

At night I sleep in a room with about six other cousins and uncles. But before we get into bed there's a whole lot of games to play. Uncle Eddie, who at eighteen is already a working man, takes out a pack of playing cards and starts shuffling them, warming them up.

Seated around the kitchen table, we do a kind of shuffling too: Denzil is sitting on Neil's lucky chair and refuses to give it up until Uncle Eddie stops shuffling and gives them a stare. Mellvin doesn't want Japan sitting next to him because Japan tends to 'peep at a man's cards'; Uncle Eddie is trying to get himself more leg room under the table. Me, I'm just happy to be included.

What will it be tonight – casino (which we call four cards) or five cards (which the cowboys call poker)? We play poker.

Neil is in the mood to show off because he's just been dealt the best hand you can think of and he's sure he's going to win. 'Oh yeah,' he says, fanning out his hand. And then he starts pretending he's John Wayne smoking a fat imaginary cigar, blowing big clouds of smoke into Mellvin's eyes. He rearranges his cards, narrows his eyes and says, 'Ahm gonna whip you all reel good!'

We all have a good laugh, even Mellvin, who pretends to wave smoke out of his eyes. But Uncle Eddie doesn't find it funny. He stamps a flat hand on the table (his other hand is holding a poor hand) and glares at Neil. He says:

'Sonny, if I ever catch you smoking I'm gonna whip your arse for real. And you and you and you!' (That's me and Japan and Doc.)

I don't like the way things are turning out here.

'Yous understand me?'

'Yes, Eddie,' we all say with a little croak in our voices.

This is a dangerous moment and I don't look at any of the others. This very morning we were in the veld smoking stompies. Does Eddie know? Did he get a whiff from one of us? Did somebody tell him? I decide there and then that I'm giving up smoking. If Doc and Japan and Neil want to carry on, let them. Me, I've had enough thank you. I know Japan will call me a sissy, but I don't care. I'm not taking any chances.

Japan is always in trouble. One day me, him and Doc are all on the roof of the shed. And won't he decide to have a pee right from up there! My ouma hears the splashing all the way from her bedroom. We hear her, far away but angry:

'Who's playing with that hose again!'

This makes us all laugh and the next thing she's in the doorway to see what's going on and she gets a full view of this yellow arc splashing down from Japan.

And what about last night! We had pap and wors and tomato gravy for supper and we were saying grace and when we opened our eyes Neil's wors had half of it bitten off. It was actually a little funny because Neil said 'Amen', opened his eyes, looked at his wors and shouted out, 'Nay, man!' and it rhymed:

'Amen ... Nay, man!'

We all laughed and that gave Japan away because he also laughed and bits of the stolen wors spurted out of his mouth.

But it was no joke for Ouma. She said to him:

'Do you want me to send you home? Just tell me and I'll pack your stuff now now now!'

I'm glad she didn't carry out her threat because, let's face it, the holidays would've been over for all of us.

When I was here on holiday last year Uncle Eddie was a boy playing with us in the street. But now he works in a shoe factory in Industria. When he comes from work he smells like leather and glue and cigarettes and his hands are rough and have tiny little cuts on them.

He's got two thick sideburns in the shape of capital Ls, and a moustache. He's taken over my oupa's shaving cup and brush, which sits on a shelf in the bathroom and which he's warned us not to touch.

'Sentimental value,' he said.

He still plays with us, but not kirriebekke and football any more. He likes playing card games like rummy and casino and poker. After his father (my oupa) died about three years ago, Uncle Eddie had to leave school to help my ouma. Sometimes I talk to him but he doesn't answer – it's as if his mind is somewhere else. Maybe he's in love or thinking about the budget. People who work are forever thinking about the budget.

A few years ago he was in Standard Six. Then one day he came home from school and told my ouma, 'I'm not going back.'

'What about your education?' she said.

'How can I worry about education when there's no bread sometimes, when they cut the lights, when you have to keep borrowing – a rand here, fifty cents there…'

She didn't say anything because he had a point.

Uncle Eddie gets his wages in a sealed envelope. Every Friday he brings it home just like his boss gave it to him. Some men steam open the envelope and take out a rand or two first and close it again. The wives are so happy for this money that they don't count it to see if it's all there. But Eddie doesn't cheat my ouma.

I like watching Eddie, this man who just a few months ago was playing soccer with us in the street. Now he comes from work and drinks tea with my ouma. He lies on his back on his bed with his hands interlocked behind his head. He stares upwards at the ceiling and sighs and sighs. It's as if, in his thoughts, he's trying to get into a house with many doors, but none will open. Every now and then he breaks into a song:

Only the lonely
know the feeling deep inside…
Only the lonely
know I cry, cry for you

In Port Elizabeth there's a coloured man who has become a famous singer. His name is Danny Williams and he used to go around barefoot selling newspapers. Then somebody heard him sing and his life changed overnight. He made a record called 'Moon River' and it became an instant hit, not only in South Africa but in Britain and America too. Everywhere people are singing:

Moon River
wider than a mile
I'm crossing you in style…

Usually it's only white people singing on the radio. But for once it's a coloured man. And every time 'Moon River' comes on, somebody shouts, 'Louder!' and the one nearest to the radio runs and puts it louder.

I like the part where he sings

Moon River
my Huckleberry friend…

Because I think it's got something to do with that book by Mark Twain, about a friendship between a white boy and a black slave over there in America.

And those newspapers that barefoot Danny Williams sold over there in Port Elizabeth? That's finish and klaar. Now he's *in* the newspapers. And according to the papers, he sings just as well as Nat King Cole and Bing Crosby and them. According to the papers, they asked Nat King Cole to also sing 'Moon River'. Mr Cole listened to Danny Williams's version, shook his head and said, 'No, I can't do better than that.'

Danny Williams was now rich and famous. He got on to a plane and went to live in England. Eddie says it's better for him there because they don't have apartheid, there's no 'Whites Only' signs all over the place. He can sit down and eat a meal in any restaurant, make records, live wherever he likes.

'He even married a white woman,' Eddie says.

Mellvin says: 'Did you hear what happened when they first kissed?'

'What?' I shake my head.

'She said: "I love you, Danny." And then he said: "I love you too, miesies."'

'Really!'

My uncles both fold up with laughter and I feel my cheeks get hot.

At the swimming pool

The next day the sun rises and burns on Corrie with a merciless fire. We feel its heat in bed and kick the blankets off us. After breakfast, lethargic with the heat, we try to sneak back into the bedrooms to lie on the beds.

But our aunts won't allow that.

'Outside!' Auntie Venecia says, pointing at the back door. 'When do yous expect us to finish our work?'

As we troop past her she gives each one of us a shove on the back of our heads, with a syllable for each shove: 'And-don't-come-back-here…' But Japan spoils her game by ducking out of her reach.

In the backyard we head for the long shadow on the other side of the shed. The neighbours around us are also in the shade of fruit trees in their own yards.

'Let's go to the swimming pool,' Japan and Doc say at the same time.

And then they start having an argument about whose idea it was first. 'Didn' I say it first?' 'Didn' I say it first?'

The truth is today all Corrie roads lead to the communal swimming pool or 'the baths'.

My ouma gives us three cents each: a cent to go in, a cent for a rented costume, and a cent for Chappies.

'And that's all I got,' she says, just in case we were thinking of nagging a few cents more out of her.

The swimming pool is in Glencairn Street up there near the community hall and the shops. It's a fifteen minute walk plus five minutes because the heat slows you down, plus five more for all the boys and girls you chat to on the way, plus another minute because Doc has a pee and he does it right there in the street while we stand around him so that girls won't see. Actually we don't have to worry about the girls seeing because whenever they see us having a pee they shout 'Sies!', cover their eyes with one hand and walk over to the other side of the street.

On the way Japan says when we all wear our rented costumes we become Joshua Mills, a boy in his class. The costumes are all blue, with a little white string that you pull to make it fit tight. All the costumes have an initial on the bum – 'JM' – which stands for Johannesburg Municipality.

Doc says to Japan, 'Hey, tell Chris about that time when Joshie copied from you in class.'

Doc and Japan swop walking places so that I can be next to Japan.

'We were doing a History test and Joshie was sitting next to me and copying from me. So I decide to trap him. Question number seven is: "Name the three ships that Jan van Riebeeck sailed to the Cape". Instead of writing *Reiger*, *Dromedaris* and *Goedehoop*, I write: *Huey*, *Dewey*, and *Louie*. And guess what?'

'He writes it?'

'He writes it!'

But we don't have time to dwell on Joshua the copycat because as we pass Mrs Thomas's house in Harmony Street, Neil remembers something and says, 'Eish!'

'What?' I ask him.

'It's exactly here,' he says, pointing to a spot on the pavement, 'exactly here where I picked up a ten cents last week Monday!'

He turns to Japan and Doc and says, 'Tell him what happened.'

'He picked up ten cents,' they both confirm.

So we stop there for two or three minutes while they recreate the scene for me, right down to placing a Coke bottle top where the ten cent coin was found and walking in the same formation. They act out the part when the money was spotted.

'Eish! We're walking an' talking, walking an' talking. And I don't know what makes me look that side. I run to it, I pick it up, I say, "Ah! Ten cents for me!"'

'Jislaaik it!'

'We hit the shops,' Japan says. 'We buy...tell him, Neil.'

Neil is only too happy to tell, making a clicking noise after each item with his fingers. 'Three cents sharps. Three ginger cakes, two apricot sweets for each one, two cents Chappies.'

'That day we were up,' Doc says.

We all inspect the lucky spot again, just in case.

'You never know,' says Neil.

My problem, I tell them, is that a Coke bottle top is silver and looks like a coin. So my heart skips a beat every time I see one.

It turns out that this is everybody else's problem too, but I feel important for having raised it first.

Today, sadly, we're not 'up'. One cent each for chewing gum is not a good situation.

As the pool comes into view Japan groans, 'Jislaaik! Everyone and his cousin is in the pool today!'

We go up to the pool's perimeter fence and peruse the action inside – as if what we see will determine whether we go in or not.

The noise is a hundred voices and the tinkle of the ice-cream vendor's bell. Towels, like bright flags, swirl around bodies, spread out on the grass.

'We forgot to bring a towel!' Japan says, and we all laugh. My ouma has exactly two towels and would never allow them to be brought here.

She says, 'I give yous money to go and get wet and now yous want to take my towel to go and dry yourselves. No!'

Japan is in charge of our meagre funds. He slides two five-cent pieces under the little window to a surly fat face on the other side and says, stooping close to the window, 'Four to go in, four coshies and two cents change.' He makes a four with the right hand, a four with the left hand and a two with the right hand.

The fat face slides our tickets and change under the window with a fat hand. The face says something that none of us can hear, but it doesn't matter because we've got what we want.

We look for our own place in the sun, a spot that we can all come to and lie down and get dry and talk. This is where a towel would've been handy – a towel marks your spot. Instead, we'll take turns staying out of the water and guarding the spot and the four cents we have for chewing gum. Neil volunteers to guard first.

Getting to the edge of the pool is the funniest part. There we all are in our coshies with the sun burning our backs and the water winking and blinking. The whole morning we've been saying let's go, let's go, let's go. But now nobody wants to dive in first. Because:

'What if the water's too cold?'

But if it is, what are all these human fish doing in the water?

'Hey, Lloyd!' Doc shouts to a boy swimming like a new frog nearby. 'How's the water?'

He spits out a 'Nice', and dives under to prove it.

And then Japan gives a scream and splashes in feet first and we follow.

Later, when I'm on guard duty, Neil comes to join me. We lie side by side on our stomachs and he turns to me and says:

'Guess what I got nine out of ten for in exams – the highest in the class?'

I say, 'Maths', because that would surprise me the most.

'Uh-uh,' he shakes his chin and water flies off it.

'What then?'

'A poem – you wanna hear it?'

It's a funny place to be listening to a poem. It's noisy and you have to watch out that people don't step on you.

'Is it long?'

'No, it's short. It's called "The 25th of December".'

He sits up and rests on his hands which he flattens on the paving. He licks his lips and begins:

The 25th of December
No one will ever forget
To remember
People doing shopping
with their children around them hopping
Toys for joy
and jolly good things
Oh what a happy time
December brings.

Mothers with babies
passing other ladies
No one's crying
No one's sighing
Because the 25th of December
No one will ever forget to remember

'It's good! I like it!' I give him a high five.

'I could've got ten out of ten. There was just a stupid comma that I forgot to put in.'

Instead of making me think about Christmas, the poem gets me thinking about my grandfather and how he died and how everybody cried. My ma cried all the time. Then she stopped crying and an old friend of hers came to sympathise and her friend says, 'You know, Shirley, that morning your dad passed away we were all late for work, half of Hamilton Street was late for work.'

'Why?' Ma asks.

'Because every morning without fail your dad used to walk down Hamilton Street on his way to work whistling, and that whistling was our alarm clock.'

She shouldn't have said that because it made my ma cry all over again.

I also heard that when my oupa died in hospital they phoned Mrs Marsh from next door because she was the only person in the street who had a phone. When she came over to break the news, my ouma was holding Neil in her arms.

'Mrs van Heerden I'm so sorry, my dear, the hospital…they just phoned me, your husband…Mr van Heerden…has just passed away…'

'What do you mean?' my ouma said.

Mrs Marsh sighed and held out her empty hands.

My ouma shouted, 'Here, hemel!' and fainted right there, and poor Neil – who had just learned to say, 'Daddy' – flew out of her arms and bumped his head against the leg of the radio and screamed.

I SNEAK A glance to see if Neil has a bump or scar from that day. I know it sounds stupid, a bump on your head six years after being flung from your mother's arms. But funny things happen when people die. Read those Boris Karloff comics and you'll tell me again.

Almost as tragic as a Boris Karloff story is the smell of food when you're hungry and the food is not yours. And mostly it's the smell of fish and chips. The vinegar smell of it drifts past our noses and is so good it stops our conversations in mid-sentence.

'Someone's eating fish and chips,' Doc says, swallowing his saliva.

'It's Havelock and them,' Japan says, spotting a bunch of boys huddled around the feast. He calls, 'Howzit, Havelock!'

Eating fish and chips seems to have made Havelock deaf.

Japan curses Havelock under his breath. Then he spots another boy in the wet loud crowds. 'Hey, Joshie!' he calls.

From among the many JMs one boy turns around and gallops towards us, water dripping from his curly, light brown hair. He grins and sniffs at my cousin with a freckled sunburnt nose.

Japan makes as if to swing two karate blows at the boy and he flings out his hand and almost trips.

'Watch it, sonny,' Japan says. He turns to me and says, 'Remember my cousin Chris from Riverlea I told you about? Who's going to be a writer?' And to me, 'This is that stupid Joshie I was telling you about, who copied *Louie*, *Huey*, and *Dewey* straight from my book.'

This introduction embarrasses me, but Joshua doesn't seem to mind; in fact, he seems quite proud and hangs around with us the whole day. He shares his fudge with us and lets us lie on his towel even before he has used it. His fudge is a tiny slab, made up of a pink layer and a white layer stuck together. There's no more than a mouthful for each of us. But it's OK because the bits of coconut hide away in different parts of your mouth and just as you've forgotten about them they pop up for you to nibble. It just proves that you don't have to know about Van Riebeeck and his three ships to be a nice guy.

Japan says to me, 'If anybody interferes with you, you call me.'

My cousin knows about these things and so do I. You go to a new township and some boy is forever walking up to you and threatening you just because you're a new face.

'But what about the big boys?' I ask him. There are boys walking about here with bulging muscles and big feet and even big teeth!

'No problem,' Japan says with a cocky flick of his wet fringe. He stands on the edge of the pool with his back to the water. 'The bigger they come, the harder they fall.' And then he falls into the water with a splash.

IT FEELS GOOD to have Japan around. He claims that he's a karate expert.

One day, in Ouma's backyard, he holds out his hand and says, 'Shake my hand.'

Sensing a trick, I refuse.

'I'm not gonna hurt you, just shake my hand.'

I shake it.

'What did you feel?' he says.

I shrug. 'Nothing. Your hand.'

'Feel here,' he says, rubbing the side of his inner palm against my hand. 'What do you feel?'

'It's sort of rough.'

He smiles and tells me why it's rough. He has taken up karate. No tutor, no club, no equipment. Just him there in my ouma's backyard, practising on the very reluctant Doc and Neil and smashing thin tomato box planks in half with karate chops and going 'Ehaah!' and jumping off the shed.

Japan demonstrates for me. He lays two planks on top of each other – because one is far too easy – between two bricks, and steps back. He stares at the planks, he narrows his eyes and bares his teeth. He goes 'Ehaah!' And his hand comes crashing down. Nothing happens to the planks but Japan gives a little yelp and shoves his hand under his left armpit.

Ouma shouts from the kitchen, 'Stop that, you'll get hurt, how many times do I have to tell you children?'

I think her warning has come too late because I hear my cousin trying to stifle a sob as he hides his face from us.

Doc and Neil look away, embarrassed and not knowing what to do.

In my granny's display cabinet in the lounge, not so far from where we are now, are photos of Neil, Doc and Japan, taken a few years ago when they were all between three and five years old. A photographer came calling at my ouma's front gate with a black pony in tow.

'Specially nice photos, madam,' he explained, 'of your nice children or grandchildren on horseback.'

Neil and Doc's photos show them sitting astride the pony terrified. Neil's mouth is wide open, caught in a scream. Doc is in tears. Only Japan is not scared, perched on top of the horse and grinning for the world and his granny to see.

So now I put my arm around his shoulder and we go behind the shed. The tears fly out from beneath his eyelashes and he wipes them away furiously, not looking at me but staying by me.

'Who got hurt?' I hear Ouma calling. 'Did one of yous get hurt?'

'Nobody, Ma!' I shout back.

'The old lady knows nothing,' Japan says with a sob. 'If I go to Japan right now they'll give me a black belt just like that.'

I'm startled – not by my cousin's claim to be a martial arts expert but by his use of the phrase 'the old lady'. It's an expression only ever used by grown-ups. My mother might say, 'How goes it with the old lady?' Or Japan's dad might say, 'Tell the old lady I'll see her next weekend'. But Japan! And with such ease.

Japan is my hero. And he doesn't have to break another plank in his life to prove it – or another bone in his body. He was just born cool.

He turns to Doc. 'Tell him what's my karate name.'

'Suki Yaki,' Doc obliges.

'Suki Yaki?'

Japan nods proudly through his tears. 'Suki Yaki. En ek vat nie kak nie,' he chants his motto.

AFTER SUPPER WE all get straight into bed because the day at the pool has sapped our energy. But the next thing I know, my uncles are telling ghost stories and we're all sitting up in bed, in the dark after Neil has put out the light for effect.

Mellvin begins and his story is about Vera the Ghost. On one cold winter's night a man drives from Coronation to Lawley, forty miles south of Johannesburg. It's past midnight and it's a dark, lonely tarred road cutting through veld. The trees are swaying shadows that emit the cries of baby animals. There's no other traffic, only this man in his black Ford. Suddenly, just before the Uncle Charlie's turn-off, he makes out a figure standing on the side of the road, a thumb pointing south.

It looks like a woman! Where could she be headed on this dark night?

The driver stops. He asks her where she's going. She's from Raven Street in Lenasia and she's on her way to Lawley. He tells her to get in. They talk for a while. She seems sad, sighing every few minutes.

'Are you OK?' he asks.

She turns to him and nods, but says nothing.

Suddenly it's hot in the car despite the cold night and the man starts to sweat.

Twenty minutes later they reach a dark gravel road which leads to a farm. It's in the middle of nowhere and too dark and too quiet. She asks to be dropped off there.

'Will you be OK here?' he asks her.

She nods. She gets off and walks away without looking back.

The next day the driver has forgotten all about the mysterious traveller. Then he sees something on the passenger seat. It's a woman's jersey, black and – he sniffs it and is repelled by its strange smell of incense. It must be hers. He decides to take it to the address in…what was it again? Raven Street, Lenasia.

He drives to Lenasia, finds the street, finds the house. He rings the doorbell. An elderly woman comes to open. Her black hair has grey streaks in it, all combed back into a bun. She's fat and she has a kitchen odour on her – onions and curry powder.

I've interrupted her cooking, the man thinks.

'Can I help you?' she asks.

'Does Vera live here?' the man says. 'I've come to return her jersey.'

The woman says nothing. Slowly she takes the jersey out of his hand, holds it to her nose and sniffs it.

'Yes, it's hers,' she says.

'She must be your daughter,' the man says.

The woman nods. 'You gave her a lift just before the Uncle Charlie's turn-off…'

'Oh, she told you?'

'No, my dear,' the woman shakes her head slowly, 'she's dead. She was killed in a car accident at that turn-off, two years ago.'

And, with a deep sigh in the dark, Mellvin indicates that his story is over. This is followed by silence.

Mellvin says, 'Did you like it?'

Even though it's dark, I know he's speaking to me. His tone for me (someone he sees once in a while) has a courtesy that he never uses when talking to Neil, Doc or Japan whom he sees every day.

He says, 'Hey!' impatiently now.

Quickly I answer, 'Yes-yes, a nice story.' But, to tell the truth, I didn't like it that much. If you ask me, the driver should not have found the woman's jersey in the car, he should have found her head – once and for all. Now that would have got us all diving under the blankets for a night of nightmares.

'Uncle Eddie, do you have a story?'

He doesn't answer and I begin to think he's fast asleep on the other bed. But eventually he says, 'Ja, I've got one.' And he takes a deep breath.

There's a whole rearranging of pillows and blankets and bums and elbows.

'This story is called: "The Hole".'

'The Hole?' What a strange title. Already I like this story.

Mrs Jackson was an old widow. She lived in a big, pretty house on the top of a hill. One summer morning she woke up and looked out of her window. And what does she see in her long driveway? A big, deep, wide hole. A hole so big that an elephant could easily fall in there. The poor woman couldn't believe her eyes. When she shouted out loud, 'I don't believe it!' there was an echo: *don't believe it believe it lieve it it!*

Mrs Jackson went to the phone and dialled a number. A man on the other end said:

'Hullo. Hole Removers, how can I help?'

Mrs Jackson tells him the problem and he says:

'No problem, madam, just give me your address and I'll send a truck right away.'

Mrs Jackson sits by her lounge window waiting for the truck. She's actually glad her children are at boarding school otherwise they would go to the edge of the hole to see how deep it is and fall in.

About twenty minutes later the truck pulls up, a big flatbed Bedford. On it she can see the words, 'Hole-a-way's Hole Removers. If it's in your way, we'll take it away'.

She waves a cheery hullo to the men. Then she goes and pours herself a cup of coffee. She's got a lot of housework this morning but that can wait because she wants to see how they're going to take that hole away.

There are four men. They get out of the truck, all in blue

overalls with the company's name and logo – a big zero – on the back. They step as close to the hole as possible and look down into it.

'Jislaaik!' one says. 'This baby's deep!' And his last word echoes: *deep-deep-deep*.

'Deeper than the one we found in Gatfontein.' *Atfontein-fontein-ntein*.

One of them sneaks up behind his friend and gives him a shove as if to push him in.

'Hey, stop that nonsense! Grow up!' *Up-up!*

Mrs Jackson can see that the poor guy got a big skrik. In fact, she herself got a fright and spilt some coffee on to her pink pyjamas.

The men start to work. The driver gets behind the wheel and and reverses as close to the edge as possible. His workmates gesture with their hands and shout, 'More…more…more…Stop!'

There's a crane on the truck, which the men attach to the hole with big steel ropes. The driver operates the crane and the men stand back and shout, 'Higher-higher-higher!' Then, 'Lower-lower!'

Mrs Jackson smiles in admiration. The hole is at last on the truck and her yard is whole again – grass, pebbles, even dog poo are all back and it's as if there had never been a hole there.

The men are full of smiles too. They're proud of a job well done and give each other high fives that crack loudly in the warm spring mid-morning. To prove to her that the hole is completely gone, one of them, the playful one, walks on to the place where the hole used to be. He jumps on it and does a little dance. And then he takes a bow.

His friends laugh at his antics and Mrs Jackson laughs too.

The driver walks across the lawn to the window. He's got a clipboard with an invoice and a carbon copy attached.

'Satisfied, madam?' he asks.

'Yes, of course,' she says and signs her name on the form.

He tears off the top copy and hands it to her. She pays him cash and tells him to keep the change.

'For Cokes for all the boys,' she says.

'Thank you, madam.'

He goes back to the truck. They wave to her and climb in.

Then, trouble! The truck is on an incline and the hole is not secured – Mrs Jackson screams, 'The hole, watch out!' But nobody can hear her. The hole slips off the truck and lands almost exactly where it was the first time. Now they will have to start all over again!

Did they hear the hole slip off? A hole doesn't make much noise when it lands, it's more like a sigh than a loud crash.

Then – an even bigger disaster – the truck, with all four men sitting up in front, rolls backwards...

'Brakes!' Mrs Jackson screams, but it's too late. The truck rolls into the hole.

In the bedroom, after a too-long silence, I ask, in the dark: 'And?'

'And,' Uncle Eddie says finally, 'that is the end of my story.'

Long after storytime, my uncles and cousin snoring away, I lie awake thinking about the hole, the men, the truck.

Great-granny, half a crown

The next morning, while we're having our coffee and bread, Ouma says:

'So where are you boys off to today?'

'Going to Granny.'

Doc and Neil (and my ma) also have a grandmother. Which of course means my granny has a mother. And that of course means that Japan and I have a great-grandmother.

Some of my friends don't even have grandparents left. And so, when I tell them about my great-grandmother, they shake their heads and say, 'Don't talk nonsense, sonny.'

But it's true, and Ma Mitchell lives right here in Coronation, with my ouma's sister, Louisa. In fact, on our way to the swimming pool yesterday we passed her house.

Ma Mitchell doesn't know we're coming. But if you're over ninety anyone can just pop in and see you – neighbours, children's children, the priest from your church, a priest from another church.

So off we go in the mid-morning sun, the warm tar on our bare feet almost too sticky and almost unbearable. We're in our shorts and T-shirts. We have two gifts for the old granny: a bottle of homemade gingerbeer, and a very tiny bottle of *Versterkdruppels*, a Dutch medicine. We also have three instructions from my ouma:

'Three drops with some sugar twice a day' (the *Versterkdruppels*).

'Tell them to dilute it with some water if they think it's too strong for her' (the gingerbeer).

'And don't ask her for money.'

(We're about to see all three instructions disobeyed in one way or another.)

The house is the same as my ouma's, the yard, the shed, even the hydrangeas with their purple and white flowers in the garden under the bedroom window.

Teenage girls are scrubbing clothes in the shade of an apricot tree, their arms in silk sleeves of foam. Bare-bottomed little boys are running around playing in mud and they've left the snot to dry outside their noses.

Everybody here speaks Afrikaans and for as long as we're here, so will we. Our Afrikaans is fluent but not as good as theirs. So our sentences will be shorter and we'll be less talkative than usual – except for Japan who'll talk to a Zulu man all day with just one word.

Boys and girls come and greet me brightly, using my nickname: 'Hullo, Kuller!' (which rhymes with Miller). But all I do is respond with a 'Hullo' that not even I can hear. I mention nobody by name. I come here only once a year and I've decided that it's not worth memorising anyone's names: there's a Kitty and a Katta and a Meidjie and even a Sonnyboy. But I'm not sure who the names belong to. I once said, 'Hullo, Jennifer', only to be told, 'I'm Jean, Jennifer's my sister'. After that I gave up.

But Japan, Neil and Doc know everyone.

'Come-come,' Japan calls to the laundry girls, 'I need my clothes washed and ironed for tonight.'

They laugh and try to blow foam in his face.

Doc says: 'I saw Bobby buying a big fruit 'n nut chocolate for that girl Sophie with the dirty fingernails.'

The girls go 'Hah!' and nod their heads as if this confirms a long-held suspicion.

Everything in the house is old. There are brownish portraits in oval frames on the dining room wall of men and women (our ancestors) who are long dead. One man has a moustache like wings. A woman has a triple chin like a stack of fatcakes. Neither of them is smiling. Whenever I take a photo somebody says, 'Say cheese!' But when these ancestors posed for these photos I don't think cheese was invented yet.

Even the knives in the kitchen drawer are from 19-Voetsek, with chipped dull yellow handles like bad teeth.

They know we've come to see Ouma Mitchell.

'She's inside,' a Ruth or Hilda says, 'in her bedroom.'

Which is exactly where she was last year.

She's sitting on the bed. But still a granddaughter calls out to her loudly, 'Is Ouma awake?' She has to ask, because these old people can sit up and sleep. There's a smell of menthol camphor in the room. The sun slants through a curtain and I can see dust particles dancing in its rays.

'The boys are here from Ouma Ruby.'

'What you say?'

'Chris is here, Shirley's son.'

'Oh ja!' says Ouma as if she'd been expecting me. She begins rubbing her arm. She doesn't turn to look at me, instead she waits for me to come into her line of vision, to break the scenery of the wall and part of an old chest of drawers that she's been staring at all morning.

'Shirley's one,' Ouma mumbles.

'And Doc and Neil and Japan, Ouma.'

She smiles and the smile fills up the grooves of the wrinkles, and bounces off the warts until her whole face is lit up.

'Shirley's one,' she mutters again, looking me up and down, inspecting me. 'You growing so fast,' she says. 'Faster than your ears.'

Japan and them have a good chuckle and I know what I'm going to be hearing all day today.

Japan gives her a hug and a kiss. Not just a peck on the cheek, a real proper kiss on the lips. I was hoping he wouldn't do that because Doc and Neil also kiss her and now I have to kiss her too – and old people have wet lips.

It's scary to see her close up. She's got so many warts there isn't space for even one more. And don't talk about her wrinkles!

She even has vertical wrinkles that run up and down between her nose to her upper lip.

'Look what we brought you, Ouma.' Doc holds up the bottle of gingerbeer.

'Is that gingerbeer?' she leans forward to get a closer look.

'Ja,' Doc says, 'I'll give it to Jean to put in the fridge…'

'No,' she snaps. 'Give it here.' She takes the bottle and lays it on the bed beside her. 'These people will just kill it with water like they did the last time.'

'And we brought this for you, Ouma,' Neil shows her the little bottle of *Versterkdruppels*.

'No. Take that back to your mother. Who said I need medicine?' She clicks her tongue.

We all laugh and she laughs too.

She turns to Japan and says, 'Ja, Japan, how are you, you old thing?'

'*You're* an old thing,' he says. 'Hey, weren't you married to Jan van Riebeeck's father?'

She laughs, happily slapping one old wrist with one old hand. The joke is not new. But my great-granny likes it so much that she provokes Japan into saying it every time he visits. He obliges and, for variety, changes the groom. The last time it was Oupa Dawie, Corrie's oldest resident who takes half a day to get from his home in Riversdale Street to the shops three streets away. Before that, she was married to Moses of the Bible.

She seems to like having been married to Van Riebeeck's father.

THIS OUMA SMILES a lot now, but she's got a sad story in her heart. My ouma told me what happened.

A long time ago, sometime in the 1920s, her husband Oupa Mitchell got sick. He had pains in his chest and they gave him lots of home remedies and medicine like the very *Versterkdruppels* that she didn't want just now, but he didn't get better. They took him to a hospital, but still he didn't improve. A few weeks later he was dead.

79

My ouma was still a little girl at the time and they were living in Sophiatown, not too far from Coronation. She says she cried and cried for her papa. My ouma says in those days the corpse (in the coffin) was brought to the house the night before the funeral for an all-night church service. Imagine sitting up all night singing 'Abide with me' and sobbing and staring at the face of your dead father?

So, my ouma says, they were all praying and sobbing and singing their hymns. When the sun comes up, they gather round the coffin for a final prayer before they go off to the cemetery. Outside, a horse and cart are waiting.

And that's when the 'dead' Mr Mitchell makes his move. He opens his eyes, gets up, looks around. The mourners are too shocked to move. He says:

'There's so many of you, surely one of you can help me out of this box.'

Of course by this time there's not 'so many' people any more because half the mourners have fled from the house screaming.

I said to my ouma: 'Maybe it's a good thing that they bring you home the night before they bury you.'

'Why d'you say that?'

'Because those old familiar smells in your house might wake you up: the smell of wors fat, stoep polish, even dirty socks.'

My ouma laughs, but her story is not over.

Sixteen years later her father got out of bed, got dressed in his blazer and hat, and went to Fordsburg – a short bus ride from Sophiatown. He went to visit his cousin and said he would be home before five in the afternoon. He never came before five nor at five nor after five. Nor the next day, nor the next week. He never came back.

'He disappeared, Ma?'

'That's it,' my ouma nods.

'But did yous look everywhere?'

'Everywhere. Sophiatown, Vrededorp, in town, everywhere. Hospitals, mortuaries. After a few months we had to give up – what could we do?'

'Shame, Ma.'

'We couldn't even bury my poor father.'

I think about this and then I remind her, 'He did have a funeral sixteen years before he died – when he got out of the coffin.'

My ouma nods and smiles.

SO HERE I am kissing my ouma's mother. Her face is sort of powdery and I wonder if one or two of those warts didn't come off and are now on my own upper lip. What I would like to do after the kiss is wipe my mouth with the back of my hand. But I can't because she's looking at me with her old but watchful eyes.

From here I can hear the distant noise of the swimming pool, the laughing and screaming. That's where we were yesterday, smack-bang in the sunshine and the water and all the other children of Corrie. And now we're here…

'Hey, Ouma's talking to you.' It's Japan nudging me.

'Yes, Ouma?'

'Did you pass school?'

By this is meant did I pass Standard Four.

'Yes, Ouma.'

She starts mumbling a few words and they turn into real sentences and I realise that she's telling us a story. I listen.

'I was at the school for one year only – I was about eight years old. Mr Pitt was our teacher. One day he comes into the class with his tennis shorts and his tennis racket. He's off to play tennis. He tells us to behave ourselves and to clean the classroom. "I want it swept and dusted and everything on its place," he says. "Understand?"

'"Yes, sir!" we all say.

'So, there he goes, off to play tennis.

'I tell the class, "Let's have a concert."

'"But Mr Pitt said…"

'"Don't worry about Mr Pitt – he's gone to play tennis."

'So we push one of the desks up in front and we use that as our stage. And the whole afternoon we're singing: "Daar kom die Alabama" and "Jou kombers en my matras", and this song and that song, and clapping and dancing.

81

'Then all of a sudden the door opens and in walks Mr Pitt. He looks around. He can't believe his eyes. The classroom is in a mess, desks pushed to one side, writing paper all over the floor, puddles of water…

'"Whose idea was this?"

'"Martha!" everybody shouts, pointing to me.

'I tell you, Mr Pitt grabs me, lays me across his lap, and starts giving me a hiding on my bum. Nya-nya-nya, I cry because it's sore. And the next thing, I start peeing all over his tennis pants and into his nice white socks and tennis shoes!'

We laugh, and Japan says, 'Sies!' and the old granny dismisses him with a wave of her hand and has a good old chuckle.

'SON.'

'Ouma?' I turn to her and see her taking something out of the pocket of her apron.

'Here.' She holds out her wrinkled fist. 'Here's a penny for you; go buy sweets.'

'Baie dankie, Ouma.' I take it and close my hand around it. But every boy and girl knows what a cent feels like, and the thing I'm holding is not one. I open my hand and take a look. It's half a crown! One of those big silver coins with King George on it. This money went out six years ago already, in 1961, when South Africa became a republic. We stopped raising the Union Jack and we got the orange, white and blue flag. We stopped singing 'God Save the Queen' and everybody had to learn 'Die Stem'. The pounds, shillings and pence disappeared and suddenly there were shiny new five- and ten- and twenty-cent coins.

But the shops will still accept this treasure that my great-granny calls a cent. The problem is, I can't accept it. It's far too much money, like getting three months' pocket money all in one day! There will be trouble for sure if I don't give it back to her now.

I start to hand it back. But before you can say Suki Yaki, a hand – a rough, tough hand – appears from nowhere and wraps itself around my hand and closes it tight.

'Japan,' I whisper to him, 'leave my hand alone.'

'No.' And his 'no' is as firm as his grip.

And then the next moment Japan has decided that it's time to go and it's, 'Goodbye, Ouma Mitchell, bye, Ruth and Jean,' and a distant cousin peeing under a nearby apricot tree.

We're shutting the Mitchells' gate when the argument starts.

'It's a mistake, Japan.'

'It's not. She gave it to you fair and square. Neil? Doc?'

Neil says, 'We'd be stupid to give it back.'

Doc says, 'Think of all the nice things we can buy. Viennas and chips …'

'Coke.'

'Red cake. Sharps toffees.'

They could've stopped at 'viennas and chips' already.

'But if I get into trouble we all get into trouble, OK?'

'That's my cousie!'

WE BUY ALL of the above, plus more. We're so loaded with parcels going from shop to shop that we begin to attract attention.

'Hey gents, where's the party?' someone calls.

It's a classmate of Doc's, sitting under an awning with other boys with grey lips and backs hunched from peeling callouses off their own feet all day.

Japan explains: 'My ouma's invited some people from the church over for tea.'

The boy is not convinced, and I don't blame him. Old ladies go for Eet-Sum-Mor biscuits and Rooibos tea, not Tiger toffees and Vicks bubblegum.

Then I spot Joshua Mills amongst them – Joshua who shared his tiny slab of fudge with us at the pool yesterday.

'Isn't that Joshie with those guys?'

Japan says, 'Ja, it's him,' and shouts, 'Howzit, Josh!'

'Let's invite him.'

Japan thinks it's a good idea. He calls, 'Hey, Josh, can I speak to you for a moment there?'

Josh and about four other guys leap up and start trotting our way.

'In *private!*' Japan says.

Neil and Doc shake their heads and mutter something about some ouens being very forward these days. Neil rearranges the cold drinks in his arms and Doc draws a pattern in the sand with his big toe. They turn their heads so that they have only a sidelong view of the boys. But not Japan, he looks them all straight in the eye.

Josh's eager companions drop off and stand around muttering their own stuff about us.

When Josh arrives all Japan says is, 'You wanna move wit us?'

Nothing more than that is necessary: the luxuries in our arms speak a persuasive language of their own. Josh slips into our walking rhythm as if he had been with us all morning.

Ten minutes later we're in the veld – where we smoked our stompies a few days ago. Whenever I come to Coronation I make at least two or three visits to this veld.

The veld lies between coloured Coronation and Afrikaner Crosby. It's about a square kilometre of overgrown grass that hides the things that the coloureds and the Afrikaners discard: bedsprings; mattresses with pee maps; kettles that can't boil any more and clocks that can't tell the time; peach and apricot trees that grew tired of bearing fruit; baby prams – but without the wheels because those were used for boxcarts; broken boxcarts; even cars – Vauxhalls and DKWs and Volkswagens, fluttering on the inside and rusty outside and sinking into the grass.

The boys and girls of Coronation who play in the veld, have named it 'the Boereveld' – a tacit acceptance that the veld was owned by the Afrikaner boys and girls rather than shared.

The feasting spot we have chosen is an Old Anglia with its odd back window that slants the wrong way. Here nobody can see or smell what we're up to – and yet from here, by parting the grass a little, we can see my ouma's house, watch the comings and goings there – and scatter and hide if we have to.

As we pass around red cakes, biscuits and cans of Fanta (nobody has to share), Joshua Mills looks stunned – he doesn't say it but we know what he's thinking.

Japan says, 'So where do you think we stole the money?'

Neil, Doc and Japan each tell a chapter of the story of how we came upon our wealth – but not me because I *am* the story!

Doc gets up and has a pee, straight into a rusty tin – and tells his part:

'And then he sees it's half a crown and he says, "Please, Ouma Mitchell, it's too much money, I'm just a poor boy from Riverlea…"'

They're exaggerating now. And it gets even more ridiculous when Joshie also tells a part of the story as if he were there.

But I don't mind. This is a Western and I'm the ouchie. They're the ouchie's sidekicks. And when they want to tell the story of how we got the loot, the ouchie doesn't have to say anything because he's the one who got it for them. So, for once, I'm cool.

'CHRIST-TER-FER!' SOMEBODY FAR away calls my name. 'And Ree-chard! Denzil! Neil!' It's my aunt Sharon. From where we're standing and drinking the last of our cold drinks, we can see her but she can't see us.

My heartbeat picks up speed. Somebody from Ouma Mitchell has come to fetch the half crown. There must be a posse waiting for me at my ouma's house right now, made up of Ruth and Jean and them. And I'm sure they're telling my ouma the shameful tale in that excitable out-of-breath way that girls have:

'He took Ouma Mitchell's pension money. We looked for him by the shops…'

'But he wasn't there…'

'But that other boy Havelock – he did tell us that he seen them buying a lot of luxuries…'

'Even a fruit an' nut chocolate.'

'Chris-ter-fer!'

'I'm coming!' I shout back, unable to bear the suspense any more. 'You see, Japan, told you…'

'Be cool. Just be cool.'

Joshie goes off in a different direction and says, 'Check yous tomorrow', but we're all too preoccupied to say 'check you' back.

We walk out from between the long grass, taking those ridiculously high steps that always make me feel silly – but right now I feel anxious.

'Why you shouting?' Neil asks his sister defensively as we approach.

'It's time for your bath,' she says. 'And aren't yous hungry? You didn't even come home for lunch.'

So there's no posse after all.

IT'S SHARON'S JOB to wash us. We get undressed and climb into the big bath, all in a row like rowers in a boat, four scrawny brown bodies with lighter bums shaped like underpants.

Sharon leaves us alone for a few minutes to splash about and pretend we're on some river or until one of us screams because there's soap in his eyes or he got scalded by a rush of hot water. Then she comes back in and foams up a washrag with Sunlight soap and says, 'Right, who's first?'

She rubs my ears too hard and I howl 'Ow!' and say, 'I wash myself at home.'

'Then go home and wash yourself,' she says. And, 'Stand up!' because she wants to wash my legs.

'Close your eyes,' I tell her.

'What for?' She rubs more soap on the rag and cackles. 'What for – because I don't see anything.'

She scrubs away streaks of urine, blotches of shop-bought jam, rust under fingernails, sweat, spit, soot, grass, street dust and veld dust, tar – a full day's fun times four going down the drain.

It will start all over again tomorrow, in the veld and the streets and the paths, collecting grease and dirt and dust. But I won't be here. This has been the last day at my ouma's.

A CLEAN CHRIS finds Ouma sitting in a warm kitchen sewing a button onto my shirt.

'You don't have to do that, Ouma. It didn't have a button when I came here.'

'But now it has one,' she says.

On the coal stove behind her a pot sizzles. She calls Sharon who comes and pours some water into the pot and the problem goes away.

'How's my mother?' my ouma asks me.

'My mother?'

'No, *my* mother. Didn't yous go visit my mother today?'

'Oh yes, I almost forgot. She's fine.'

I watch the needle and its cotton tail going up up up and winking in the setting sun.

'You going home tomorrow?'

'Ma?'

'I said you're going home tomorrow?'

'Ja, Ma. Ma.'

'Yes, son.'

'I'm gonna save up my pocket money and buy you a present.'

'Ag shame, you don't have to do that.'

'But I want to.'

'And what are you going to buy your old ouma?'

'A record with your favourite song on it.'

'Hah! And what's my favourite song?'

'The one that you sing every Sunday morning.'

'And what song is that?'

'Where they keep singing: "See the world through lace-covered windows."'

My ouma laughs so much that she has to put her needlework aside. I don't understand grown-ups when it comes to jokes: you can tell them the best joke you've ever heard and they won't even smile. But tell them something serious and they can shake with laughter.

My holiday is over. I've been here for a week but it feels like no more than two days. I don't really want to go back home, but school is starting soon. I pack all my clothes and stuff into my packet – underpants, shirt, T-shirt. All the clothes are there, but one of my comics is missing. Ouma orders everyone to look for it, and even joins the search herself.

'Where did you see it last?' she wants to know.

Now there's a question I hate. If you lose something, like a comic or a shoe or a snakes and ladders counter, people always want to know where was the last place you saw it or put it. They think that's where they will find it, like:

'I put it under the bed.'

'So let's go and look there. Aha, there it is!'

My ouma can't read so she says, 'What's on the cover?'

'Spiderman is crawling up a very high building and…'

'What does he look like?' she wants to know.

I can't believe that someone doesn't know what Spiderman looks like.

'Ouma he's one of the most famous crime-fighters in the whole universe!'

She laughs and says, 'Oe genade! Somebody please pass me the dictionary.'

I notice that Doc isn't looking hard enough and I suspect that he's hidden it away because he wants to keep it for a while. Or he's lent it to one of his friends who hasn't brought it back in time. But I have no proof so I don't say anything.

I say goodbye to my ouma and kiss her.

Me, Japan, Doc and Neil swop high fives and punches on the arms and they call me their 'laaitie'.

My ouma says, 'When are you coming again?'

'I really don't know, Ouma.'

'You don't know or you don't want to come again?'

'I'll see, Ouma. I'm going to be busy this year, Standard Five isn't easy and…'

'But you're not going to do your schoolwork during the holidays too, aw!' She looks a little hurt. 'You must come visit your ouma again Easter maybe?'

'I don't know, Ouma,' I say with a tired sigh. 'I'll see.'

But she knows as well as I do that I'll be there for the Easter holidays.

She wipes the sweat off my nose, and I kiss her.

UNCLE MELLVIN AND I begin the long walk home, across the railway line, through Industria, over the non-European bridge.

We don't talk as much as we did when we came to Coronation a week ago. He's got a lot of things to think about and so do I.

I think about Derek and Shaune and Alison and I begin to miss them and I'm glad that I'll be seeing them soon. I miss my ma and my dad and Conos and them. Has anything interesting happened while I was away? Derek will fill me in.

I think about Uncle Eddie's story about the hole. I also think about my great-grandfather and how he got up out of his coffin – and then a few years later disappeared. And then I realise, with a strange thrill, that the two stories – the hole and the great-grandfather story – are in some ways the same! They're both funny and sad at the same time.

I turn to Mellvin. 'What are you going to be when you finish school?'

'Anything,' he says. 'Welder, clerk, whatever pays the most. I have to help the old lady.'

'I'm gonna be a writer.'

'I know, you told me.'

'Well the last time I told you I wasn't really sure, but this time I'm sure.'

'Hey listen here, the next time you tell me something, only tell me when you're sure.'

He can see that I didn't like that, so he says quickly:

'But a book, a book is not that easy to write. You have to write a lot of pages.'

'I know.'

'What are you gonna write?'

I'm silent for a while as I think about this.

'You see, you don't even know what you're gonna write.'

'I do. I'm just thinking of a way to make it simple so that you can understand.'

'Hey, sonny!' He aims a smack at the back of my head but I skip out of the way in time.

AT HOME EVERYBODY'S happy to see me. Derek and Shaune hadn't been on speaking terms for a day or two, over some missing money from somebody's moneybox. But they're so eager to give me new Riverlea gossip that they start chatting to each other.

'Sheba [the Wilsons' dog] has six puppies.'

'Mr Gallon [one of our schoolteachers] was so drunk last Saturday, he fell out of a car.'

'I [Derek] caught a ten-cent strokie by the shops.'

Ma is also pleased to see me and she asks, 'So how's the old girl?'

I pass on a few messages from my ouma – 'Auntie Jenny found a job at last, in an envelope factory. And Mrs Green is back in hospital.'

Even my dad runs his fingers through my hair and turns down the radio so that we can chat for a while. I use the opportunity to announce my future career.

'I'm going to be a writer when I grow up.'

'That's good,' he says. 'I think you'll make it.'

'But I'm a coloured.'

He laughs and says, 'Really!'

In the kitchen Ma has been listening to us and says, 'He's full of surprises this child.'

'Yous don't understand what I mean…all the writers are white. Even the characters in the books, the boys and girls who have adventures and stuff.'

'That's not true,' Dad says. 'In America there are quite a few black writers.'

'Like who?'

He thinks and says, 'Now you're asking me something.'

I can see he's not even thinking; he just doesn't know. He knows about American jazz, Louis Armstrong and Duke Ellington and them, but not about writing.

'What about here in South Africa?'

'Oh yes, there are one or two. They write stories for *Drum* magazine.' And then his face lights up as he remembers something. 'When I was at school there was a writer who came to our school.

A coloured guy, his name was Peter Abrahams. He wrote a book about growing up in Vrededorp, and some other books. But the government banned his books.'

'What's that?'

'They stopped the shops from selling the books.'

'Is the government allowed to do that?'

He laughs. 'The government is the government; they can do whatever they like.'

'That's not fair.'

'That's what Peter Abrahams said. So he left the country and went to live in England or America.'

'Like that singer Danny Williams!'

'Exactly! But a few years before Peter Abrahams left, our school principal invited him to speak to us in assembly.'

'Are you serious?'

He nods and takes a puff of his Gold Dollar cigarette.

'What did he say?'

'He said…' he thinks hard for a moment, rubbing his sandpaper chin. 'He said, "Good morning, boys and girls!"' He laughs at his joke and of course in the kitchen Ma has a good chuckle too. And so do I – but not for long before I get serious again.

'What did he say in his speech?'

'*Now* you're asking me something,' he says – which he always says when he doesn't know the answer to something. I wish I could say that at school:

Teacher: 'Chris, in what year did the Anglo-Boer war begin?'

Me: '*Now* you're asking me something.'

'What will you write about?' Dad asks me.

Everyone keeps asking me that and I never have an answer for them. But this time I do.

'Stories that are funny and sad at the same time.'

My father frowns.

'Like Sad Sack and Boris Karloff in one.'

'I told you, Nick,' Ma says, 'this child is full of surprises.'

Eureka! Socrates!

The other day I borrowed a book called *One Hundred Great Lives* from the library, and what a find it turns out to be! For a while it becomes my favourite book and I renew it two or three times before I decide to give somebody else a chance.

I flip through the book and stop on Socrates. Socrates! I remember my granny's front garden in Coronation. Vincent's graffiti-spattered shirt and me circling him and reading it all and being puzzled by 'Socrates' who ate 'hemlock'. That was many months ago, but maybe, at last, I have the answer right in front of me.

I begin to read about Socrates and his remarkable life, how he was an extremely clever man, in fact a philosopher, who lived in Athens in Greece thousands of years ago. He used to hang around in public squares speaking to people, young and old, about life and how to understand the world around you.

In those days the Greeks believed in myths and in gods such as Zeus, Poseidon, Apollo and Aphrodite. But Socrates, in his sandals and his toga on the square would scoff: 'All rubbish! These gods don't exist.'

Rubbish! You couldn't say such things about the gods. You could get into serious trouble. And that is exactly what happened to Socrates.

The authorities get to hear about this Socrates and how he's poisoning the minds of the young people of Athens. They put him on trial and find him guilty. Then they say to him: 'Look, if you make a public statement taking back all those things you've been saying about our gods, we'll let you go. But if you refuse you must die.'

Rather than give up his beliefs and opinions, Socrates chose death. The method of execution in those days was to eat poison. And guess what that poison was called?

Goodbye Maria

We once had a maid called Maria.

This sounds like the song from *West Side Story*, but it's true. Ma always says Maria was the best housekeeper we ever had. When we left our home in the mornings, the house was a mess – breadcrumbs on the kitchen table and on the floor, squeezed-out teabags drying on the kitchen sink, coffee-stained cups everywhere, kitchen, bedroom and dining room.

Blankets and pillows strewn on the floor, schoolbooks forgotten on tables and chairs, a sock here, a shirt there.

When we came home in the afternoons, the place was transformed, like a house in a fairytale with a kind fairy and a happy ending.

I could see the magic from a mile away. The front stoep, three simple red slabs, shone brightly, like the gloss on my aunt's lips when she went dancing at the Chez Gaye.

The windows sparkled and when the sun reflected in them you blinked and had to look away. Inside, the furniture shone, the old sideboard as well as the almost new Pilot radio. The linoleum floors, the stove.

Maria's instructions to us – me, Derek, Shaune and Alison – began at the front door, in the afternoon when we came from school, with the words:

'Come around the back.'

'It's me, Auntie.' (Ma had insisted that we call her Auntie and not by her name as she was a grown woman and not a friend.)

'I know it's you. But still I say, come around the back.'

When I came around to the back, she stood waiting, to explain:

'When you children come from school, you are to come around the back. After I have cleaned the house, I don't want dirty shoes messing up the lounge.'

'Yes, Auntie.'

Other instructions included:

'Stamp your shoes before you come inside the house.'

'Eat at the kitchen table, not on the beds, in the lounge, outside.'

'Put your dirty socks in the washing basket.'

'Take off your school uniform and hang it in the wardrobe before you go out.'

One afternoon, Conos popped in to visit. He popped in most days, but this would be the first time he would meet Maria.

He greeted her politely, then asked, 'Is Chris in?'

'Yes,' she said, but remained standing in the doorway when she should be stepping aside.

I wasn't there to witness this embarrassing moment, but I know Conos well enough to see in my mind's eye how the situation unfolds. He tries to slip past the left side of her, but she moves closer to the door frame. He tries the other side, but she now closes that gap too. This is a silly joke that people in door frames will sometimes play on a visitor. But first Conos has to know if it is a joke. And in order to do so he steps back to get a good look of Maria's face.

This woman is not playing a game, he realises. So he shouts over her shoulder, 'Chris!'

To cut a long story short, Maria Rule Number Whatever was: 'No neighbourhood kids in this house after I've cleaned it!'

Maria also did other things that impressed Ma: she sewed buttons on shirts, rearranged furniture to create more space, discarded old shoes and stuff that should have been thrown away years ago.

One afternoon we came from school to find a big pot of mageu bubbling contentedly in a pot underneath the kitchen table. What a treat for us.

(Ma had mixed feelings about the mageu though – 'It takes a month's supply of sugar in one week!')

But Maria was still the Number 1 housekeeper.

Before she leaves in the afternoons to catch her train to Soweto, Maria sits for a while in the lounge. She doesn't joke or make small talk or ask things about us, our parents or school. She is a pretty, mysterious statue in smart black shoes, a bright floral dress, a black beret, and face shining from the skin-lightening cream she rubs on it every afternoon.

One day she does break her silence. From an armchair she stares up at the pelmet above our lounge window. It is an eye-catching object that is almost twice the length of the window. Its edge has been carved in a way that gives the impression of flowers dangling down from it. It is a work of art, and Maria herself keeps it shiny.

'Who made this?' she asks me.

'My father,' I tell her, happy and eager to talk to Maria.

She pulls a face, and says, 'It should be in my house.'

'Why?'

'Because it's too pretty for this house.'

I don't know what to say.

'My house is nicer than your house,' she says.

Maria left soon after that remark. Ma might have missed her, but not me.

Hullo Agnes

Hiring a housekeeper is a complicated business. Women come knocking on the door all the time looking for work. Mrs Baines from down the road hired a woman who came knocking at their door.

'What's your name?' Mrs Baines asked her.

'Patience, madam.'

'You know how to wash and iron?'

'I know it, madam.'

'You don't burn clothes?'

'Never, madam.'

'Who did you work for before?'

'Mrs van Rensburg, madam. In Mayfair.'

'A white woman.'

Patience nods.

'Why did she fire you?'

'She did not fire me, madam. They move to Durban.'

'Madam' looks her up and down. She's very well dressed – although a little young. Their boyfriends come visiting when everyone's gone to work and to school. The boyfriends are trouble.

'Do you have a boyfriend?'

Patience does not have a boyfriend.

'OK, eighteen rand per week.'

Patience nods.

Patience works for two weeks earning a total of thirty-six rand. One Monday afternoon Mrs Baines's son Walter comes home from school to find that they had been robbed. Patience was nowhere to be seen. And also missing were all their best clothes. The wardrobes are empty and the doors squeak as they flap in a gust of wind from the open windows.

Walter goes to the public phone at the community hall and phones his ma at Dugsons. He's not a good communicator – he says:

'Ma, all our clothes are gone.'

His ma says, 'Ask Patience where she put them.'

SO, THE BEST thing to do is to do what Ma does. The Conways have someone called Jane who has been working for them for years and years. Ma goes over to the Conways and asks Auntie Freda if she can talk to Jane about getting a housekeeper. Jane says she has a sister who is looking for a job.

'Ag please Jane, can you bring her on Monday morning – I'm desperate.'

'I'll bring her, madam.'

So, on Monday afternoon, I've totally forgotten that a new housekeeper awaits at home. Conos and I are walking home from school, when he decides to pop in at my home – it could be to fetch a piece of string or a book or just to hang out a little longer – and that's when we both meet Agnes.

She's at the kitchen table smearing butter and apricot jam on to about a dozen slices of bread.

She's a small dark woman in a brown beret. Her pink overall once upon a time had five buttons but only two have survived. Her eyes are puffy as if from lack of sleep or too much drinking. But, no matter, she grins at me and Conos.

Before I can utter a word, she sticks two slices of bread together – one smeared with jam and the other with butter – and shoves it into Conos's hands with the words, 'Here, Chris, take your lunch.'

'I'm not Chris,' he says, but bites a big half-moon out of the sandwich before anybody can object.

Agnes laughs with delight and does a little two-step dance. 'First mistake of the day I make,' she says. 'Then where is Chris?'

'Me, I'm Chris,' I point at my chest, annoyed. 'If he's not Chris then who do you think I am?'

'OK. But I must ask, I don't want to make a mistake again.'

I don't believe this. I turn to Conos, but he just pulls a face as if to say, she does have a point. And he takes another bite.

She hands me some bread too. And calls Derek, Shaune and Alison to get theirs. Derek is doing his homework and Shaune, my brother tells me, has gone looking for Alison next door.

Agnes pours tea for all of us – and before I can stop her, she dumps three spoons of sugar in all the cups.

'I take two,' I tell her.

She stops stirring.

'I take two sugars – three is too sweet for me.'

'It's not too sweet for me,' she says, and takes a sip from her own cup to prove it.

I'm glad Conos is with me rather than Vino. Vino's always a little uptight and would have gone and told half the people of Riverlea that the Van Wyks have a weird black woman from Soweto cleaning for them. But Conos seems amused – and maybe even happy after his unfriendly encounters with Maria.

After his bread and tea he gets up to leave. 'Thanks for the lunch, Agnes,' he says, and to me, 'Check you, kabawo.'

I leave half a cup of tea at the kitchen table and get up to see him out. When we're out of earshot I stop and put my hands on my hips and say, 'What do you think of this woman?'

He lets his eyebrows arch upwards. 'She's a little drunk.'

'What?'

'I'm telling you.'

'How d'you know?'

'I smelt.'

CONOS IS NOT more observant than me – we just seem to notice different things. One day when we walked past the EBC Church, Conos read out the words underneath the cross:

Evangical Bible Church

'Evangelical,' I corrected him.

'What d'you mean?'

'Look carefully.' Then I took him through it syllable by syllable 'E-VAN-GEL…'

'OK, I get it,' he said.

Now, standing at the side of the house he tells me this. And I'm a little embarrassed and I don't want to stand and chat some more; I want to get back in the house and have a sniff for myself – and I don't care if she sees me sniffing. I say a quick, 'Check you', turn on my heel and go back inside.

'What did he say to you?' Agnes wants to know, washing dishes.

Does she know what we just said about her?

'He said goodbye.' If this woman really is drunk, as Conos claims, I swear I'll tell Ma.

'What word did he use: ka-what, ka-what?' she prompts me.

'Kabawo.'

'What's that?'

'You won't understand…'

'Why won't I understand?' She's drying a bunch of teaspoons and knives and dropping each one into a dresser drawer with a bright steely noise. She's working fast and I can tell she's in a hurry. But still she wants an answer.

'That's just slang,' I explain slowly. 'Kabawo is not really a word, it's the way we talk in the streets.'

'Serious?'

'Yes, serious.'

I turn to go when she says:

'It *is* a word.'

'What did you say?'

'Kabawo is a word.'

'What do you mean?'

'It's a Xhosa word and it means: "my father's son". You see when a Xhosa man greets…'

'I know what you mean,' I snap, and she looks back at me with her puffy eyes.

'Why didn't you tell me in the first place?'

'In the first place?'

I ignore her. I'm sure my face has gone red and I don't want her to see it. I fetch the thickest book I have, which happens to be *One Hundred Great Lives,* and bring it to the kitchen table. I'll show Miss Puffy Eyes who's the clever one around here. I begin to page through it, past Winston Churchill, Catherine the Great of Russia, Mahatma Gandhi, staring back at me through round glasses.

But I can't take my mind off 'kabawo'. All over Riverlea, right now, some boy is greeting another with a 'Heit, kabawo'. Between me, Conos, Vino and Derek and them we must have used the word a thousand times in the last week thinking it's slang. Then along comes this woman and tells me it's an actual word.

She's humming a tune, trying to attract my attention. I ignore her and try to read.

'Jo!' she shouts.

I look up.

'That's a big book. What is the name of it?'

I hold it up so that she can see for herself.

She squints at the title and says, 'Say again?' I don't think she can read English.

'*One Hundred Great Lives.*'

'Is it a story?'

'It's a hundred stories.'

'A hundred?'

She seems genuinely interested (although I'm still suspicious after that kabawo thing). I explain it to her – that these are short biographies of one hundred great people.

'This one is William Shakespeare.' I show her a picture.

She skips over to the table and has a quick look.

'Mhm,' she says, 'long hair.'

'Don't worry about his long hair. He was a writer who lived long ago. He wrote beautiful stories. And I'm also going to be a writer.'

She nods. 'Show me another one.'

'This one is Edward Jenner. He was a scientist.'

'A what?'

'A man who works with medicine and stuff.'

'Very good,' she says. 'Thank you Mr Teacher.'

I smile and watch her skip out of the kitchen in her bare feet. I may not have known about 'kabawo', but I do know about lots of other things. A pity she can't see me in action when *Pick a Box* is on the radio with Duggie Laws:

For which movie did John Wayne win an Oscar?

'True Grit.'

On which farm was gold discovered in the Transvaal?

'Randjeslaagte.'

Who said: Give them cake?

'Marie Antoinette.'

I don't get them all right. But the more I read the more I'll get right – that's what Mrs Abrahams always says.

I HEAR THE sound of running water in our backyard. It must be Alison and her friends messing about with water. And if Ma comes home and my sister's chest is all wet and she starts coughing then I'll be told, 'You're supposed to be the eldest…'

So I get up and stick my head out of the kitchen door. But it's Agnes, bent over the tap and washing her feet with a rough stone. She looks up.

'I'm thinking to ask you something.'

'What?'

'Is Shaka in that book?'

I laugh.

'I'm serious.' She shakes a foot dry and puts it into an old scuffed shoe. She looks up at me, waiting for an answer.

'He's not!'

'Why?'

She turns the tap and the water spurts out loudly. Who was Shaka anyway? A Zulu chief, that's all I know about him. I don't even know how I came upon that small piece of information. We don't learn about the Zulus or the Sothos or the Tswanas at school – or the coloureds for that matter.

All we learn about is white people. Jan van Riebeeck who sailed from Holland and discovered the Cape – and all the other white people who did this and that and the other.

'Was Shaka great?' I ask her.

'Yes.'

'Why?'

'I got eggs to lay and chickens to hatch,' she says.

'You got what?'

But she grabs her bag, as tatty as her shoes, and disappears around the house calling out to her friends who are waiting for her in the street.

She *is* drunk, I decide. Or mad.

When Ma comes from work, she wants to know if Agnes had come to work.

'Yes, Ma, she was here.'

'Do yous like her?'

'Ja, I do, she's nice.'

19-Voetsek

Uncle Arnie from next door has a Vauxhall from 19-Voetsek. That means so long ago that it's hard to remember the year. It just about goes. Just about. Just-just about. It's rusty, it has about twenty per cent of its green paint missing, and there are places where you can see it was once light blue. Uncle Arnie's friends say, 'Hey Arnie, isn't this the thing that Jan van Riebeeck came to South Africa in?'

Uncle Arnie laughs good naturedly and then he says, 'Carry on. But next time you're walking home late at night from up there near the police station, and I pass you, I'm not stopping to give you a lift.'

Uncle Arnie calls his car the Piskarretjie – and there's a good reason why. When he goes to Corrie or Noordgesig and he's in a good mood, he takes us along.

'Jump in, my laaities,' he says.

We don't ask where we're going because anywhere out of Riverlea is as good as the coast. So we pile in. Twenty minutes later, we're in Main Reef Road, riding past the furniture factories on the one side and the long railway line on the other.

We're six or seven on the back seat, farting and teasing each other. Crowbar says:

'Eish, look at that kwaai Mercedes!'

I look quickly, but there's no Mercedes and Crowbar says, 'Apie skaapie.'

Well I may be an apie skaapie, but it's better to be in the car being fooled than alone in Riverlea's dust. The worst thing is to suddenly find out that everybody's gone with Uncle Arnie to Noordgesig.

'Agnes, have you seen Derek anywhere?'

Without looking up from her ironing, she says, 'I think he's gone with Mr Conway.'

'What!' My heart sinks. 'Why didn't you tell me?'

'Aw! You were not here to tell.'

'When did they go?'

'Now-now-now. You just missed them.'

When they come back they tell you what a good time they all had.

'Uncle Arnie bought us chips!'

'We saw a helluva accident there in Main Reef near Crawley's Garage.'

'We sat in the shade of a peach tree eating ripe peaches the whole time.'

'We did this…'

'We did that…'

You know half of it is lies, but they still manage to make you feel sick from having been left out.

But today I'm far from left out, I'm in the mix.

We're ten minutes from Noordgesig and Rathead's got a pee, a big pee; he can't wait.

'Why didn't you pee in Riverlea?' Uncle Arnie asks, gnashing away at his gears.

'Uncle Arnie was in a hurry, Uncle Arnie.'

'See that hole in the floor?' Uncle Arnie says.

We can't miss it, it's as big as a saucer, and Main Reef Road is rushing by underneath it.

'Pee through that hole, my laaitie,' Uncle Arnie says. 'But aim straight.'

Rathead doesn't wait for small change. He pees through the hole. And of course, now we all have a pee and we're leaving behind a long wet stripe in Main Reef Road while Uncle Arnie is laughing his head off.

Uncle Arnie buys these skorokoros from friends and white people. He gets someone to tow them to his backyard and he spends his weekends trying to fix them up. Most don't ever ride again, but Uncle Arnie has managed to bring this sputtering thing back to life for a month or two.

He drains all the old oil from the cars and keeps it in a drum in the yard.

'Why are you keeping that dirty oil, Uncle Arnie?' we ask him.

'For Oortjies,' he says.

Half of the township's dogs from time to time walk about with brandsiekte – their coats peel away and it looks as if they've been in a fire. But never Oortjies. Because he's protected with SABS approved, ten-year-old, used, but freshly drained Valvoline.

Uncle Arnie corners Oortjies in the yard, pours the oil all over the bewildered dog, and rubs it in with elbow grease.

That's why Oortjies is the champion of dogs in Riverlea. And why Uncle Arnie is the champion of uncles.

A prayer for Bruno

When the girls of Riverlea play skipping rope in the streets, they stuff their skirts into their panties, jump to the slap-slap rhythm of the rope, and chant:

Wie-de-we
die hond skiet die kat
met die gun...

It's a nonsense song about a dog shooting a cat with a gun. But nobody takes any notice. Maybe it's because the dogs of Riverlea are crazier than the dog in the skipping rope song.

Every family has a dog and ours is Bruno van Wyk (a dog always has the same surname as its owners). He's a handsome brown Alsatian with a thick mane, like a lion. He follows my brother Derek everywhere.

For a while Derek was famous in our family and his class for the way he recited a poem called 'Freddie'. In the poem little Freddie's ma scolds him for playing around at home when he should be making his way to school. It goes:

Freddie it is getting late
Are you swinging on the gate
Where's your schoolbag, Freddie

One afternoon Mrs Keston was doing recitation in the class. The boys and girls were coming up to the front one by one, in alphabetical order, reciting a poem for a mark in Orals.

Some mumbled their way through their poem, others skipped lines, one boy even forgot the entire poem and spent the time it would have taken to recite the poem grinning at the class.

Derek, being a V for Van Wyk, was second-last – before Patricia Wentzel. He goes up to the front, rolls his shoulders and begins to chastise Freddie for being such a laggard. He shouts out the poem. The class is transfixed and Mrs Keston, watching from her desk, sees a vein on his temple begin to throb.

After the recitation Mrs Keston takes him by the hand and marches him to all the classes in the school where my brother has to give a repeat performance over and over again – as an example of how a poem should be delivered.

That's how fame first came to Derek. But when Bruno arrived Derek's fame spread even wider – for being one of the few in Riverlea who owns a real thoroughbred Alsatian.

Derek plays with Bruno for hours. He stands in our backyard and throws a tennis ball over the roof of our house. Bruno darts around to the front – and seconds later he's back with the ball, dripping with dog spit, wedged between his teeth for Derek to throw it again.

Derek calls him 'my boy' and strokes his thick coat. Every morning Derek calls him to his side, prises his jaw open and spits in his mouth. Bruno gulps it down eagerly.

'What's that for?' Crowbar asks him.

'So that he'll always be loyal to me,' Derek explains.

Crowbar turns to Pikkie and says, 'Open your mouth.'

Pikkie swears at him.

THERE ARE MOSTLY brakkies in Riverlea – no Scottish this or German that or Irish whatever. These are just Riverlea dogs, so *gemaak en so gelaatstaan* (made like that and left like that). So Bruno stands out.

We got Bruno from my dad's white boss.

'Feed him well,' Mr Bothner said, 'and make sure he gets his Bob Martin tablet every day.'

'Of course, Mr Bothner,' Dad said. But when he's back in Riverlea and telling his friends the story he scoffs and says, 'Bob Martin! The only time this dog will get a Bob Martin is when he goes out and actually bites somebody called Bob Martin.'

And as for 'Feed him well', Bruno gets what all Riverlea's dogs get – the supper's scraps served up in the dustbin's lid. Stand in any backyard at around seven o'clock in the evening and you'll hear the same sound coming from all the other backyards – a fork scraping the scraps from a plate.

A dog has to make sure he or she is there when the scraps hit the lid. If you're roaming the streets, sniffing bums and picking fights at supper time, another dog will be there to clean that lid for you.

The dog that is always waiting to eat Bruno's food is my friend Jerome's dog, Oortjies Conway. He's half the size of Bruno and his dirty brown coat is made up of short spiky hair. I suppose you could say he doesn't have hair and complexion. He's got sores from his grey nose all the way to his stumpy tail from fights and licking into pilchard and corned beef and even condensed milk tins.

Bruno might have the looks but Oortjies has the survival skills.

The People's Dispensary for Sick Animals comes to Riverlea once a month. It's like the SPCA on wheels. They park their van in the patch of bare veld opposite the shops. They swing open the two big doors at the back and lower a set of steel steps. And before you can say 'pavement special' there's a long line of boys and their dogs coming for their monthly check-up. There's a dog with one eye, another with a mangled paw, a knife wound, one that had bleach thrown over its body. Some of the boys themselves don't look much better than the dogs.

Oortjies goes to the PDSA van on his own – but not for a check-up. He only goes to check out the girl dogs.

Then there's a dog called Boer, a white woolly dog with red eyes that lives down in Gironde Street. My friend Peter's ma named the dog Boer. Mrs Williams is a shop steward in a clothing factory and, people say, a very political person. She named the dog Boer because, she says, everywhere she goes boere are ordering her around: her boss, policemen, even Afrikaner post office workers who haven't passed Standard Six. So, she says, it's nice to shout 'Boer!' and see a boer come running to her.

Everybody laughs at the dog's name, but a name like that can get a man into big trouble. One afternoon Peter runs out of the house shouting, 'Boer, Boer!' Boer comes running to him from the street. But when Peter looks up he can't believe his eyes – standing by their gate is a real boer – an Afrikaner man. And he's not amused.

Peter is shocked. Afrikaners in the township are a rare sight. The only ones you ever see around here are policemen, cursing and chasing after the street gangs who smoke dagga and roll dice behind the shops. This Afrikaner is in a grey suit. He has a clipboard in one hand and a pen in the other. His face is an angry red blotch (the hot summer sun is also to blame) and his brown moustache is bristling. He doesn't say anything, just stands there by the gate like the Hertzog tower in Brixton staring down at poor Peter, waiting, it seems, for an explanation.

Peter strokes Boer, looks up at the man, strokes Boer. Then he says:

'Ag moenie worry nie, meneer, sy tweede naam is Boesman.' (Don't feel offended, sir, his second name is Bushman.)

THEN THERE'S JACKO Myburgh, Marlon's dog. Jacko is white with brown patches – a Jack Russell.

The day Marlon gets Jacko, me, Crowbar, Toolbag and Hippie go to Marlon's yard to check out this new dog. We watch Jacko sniffing around our bare feet and dirty takkies while Marlon gives us some quick facts about this breed of dog.

'There are two kinds of Jack Russell; the one with the long legs and the one with the short legs…'

'And then there's Jacko whose legs are medium!' Crowbar says. We laugh so much that Jacko himself decides to go and sit on a coal bag where he gets very dusty.

Marlon bristles and his eyes go narrower than usual and he says to Crowbar, 'Are you trying to be funny, sonny?'

This is a stupid thing to ask Crowbar – far from *trying* to be funny, he's just said the funniest thing we've all heard in months.

Marlon is without doubt the biggest and strongest amongst us, and so Crowbar quickly apologises. But the damage is done: when Marlon is not around we all call Jacko 'Medium' and this confuses the poor dog.

Marlon is in my class even though he's two years older than me. He gets lots of things wrong in class – sums, words, dates, things like that – but he says he doesn't care because when he grows up he wants to live in the jungle like Tarzan. He says he doesn't need education, he just needs to know which roots he can eat and which ones are poisonous.

Marlon struts about bare-chested in the backyard, swinging and jumping from their apricot tree.

Tarzan goes about the jungle with a monkey on his shoulder. Marlon tries to put Jacko on his shoulder, but poor Jacko keeps falling off.

Marlon's ma, Auntie Gladys, has two cats, a black one and a white one. They lie around the house licking their paws and looking intently into a space in front of them as if they are thinking about serious things.

Eventually Jacko also lies around the house like a cat. He stares at Auntie Gladys while she knits as if wondering: is that jersey for me or for Marlon?

One day our teacher Mrs Turton gives us homework: 'Write five sentences about your dog.'

When I get home from school, I write my sentences quickly because I want to go and play football in the street with Conos and Crowbar and Peter and Marlon and them. I go over to Marlon's house to fetch him for our game. But he's struggling with the sentences and his ma warned him:

'No going out to play until you finish your homework.'

All he's got so far is the heading on top of the page and centred:

My Dog Jako.

'You forgot the c,' I tell Marlon.

He clicks his tongue and proceeds to correct it.

I look up at the picture of Jesus Christ on the dining room wall, looking calm and collected. I listen to the click-clack of Auntie Gladys's knitting needles coming from the kitchen. I study Marlon's ma and dad's wedding portrait. She's pretty and happy. He's shorter than his new bride – maybe that's why he looks so cross. When I look down again at what Marlon's done, it reads: 'My Dog Jakco.'

'You put the c in the wrong place.'

'Huh?' he says and pulls his head back from the page to get a different perspective.

'It's supposed to go *before* the k – like pack and back.'

He sighs and says, 'Next time don't be shy to point.'

He proceeds, with his blue ballpoint pen, to scratch out the c. But instead he paints it out and if you see the big blue blob in its place, you'll agree that the c was better. The day before yesterday Mrs Turton gave Trevor Abrahams a few on his knuckles with a one-foot-long white Department of Coloured Affairs plastic ruler for doing exactly the same thing. The only difference is that Trevor's blob was green.

Marlon utters a really bad word, which we mostly use when we're playing football and someone has kicked our ankles in a tackle – and only when the adults aren't around.

From the kitchen his ma says, 'Hey, d'you want me to put chillies in that filthy mouth of yours?'

'It's this Jacko, Ma,' Marlon shouts.

'How can it be Jacko if he's lying right here?' his ma says.

I call out to her, 'It's the *word* Jacko, Auntie Gladys!'

'Is that so?' she says, and the click-clack-click of the needles starts up again.

Marlon says, 'Right, gimme a sentence.'

'Jacko has brown and white patches.'

He writes and writes – and stops. 'Spell "patches".'

I spell it for him.

While we're thinking of another sentence, he says, 'Hey, this could've been two sentences: "Jacko has brown patches" and "Jacko has white patches."'

'Don't worry, we'll find four more. Ah, what about: "I want Jacko to be a monkey."'

'Good one.' Marlon writes it down. Then he thinks of one and blurts it out proudly:

'Jacko guards our house at night.'

Jacko does no such thing, but I nod my approval. He writes 'gards' but I don't correct him this time because I don't want to see any more painting. And, to be honest, I'm not so sure on which side of the a the u goes.

Marlon is getting the idea now and his face lights up as another sentence pops into his head.

'What about: "Jacko once bit a horse."'

We both laugh out loud, our chins low on the table, and then Marlon writes it down. We need one more, and I say:

'The horse bit Jacko back.'

Marlon writes it down right away, while we both laugh our heads off.

Marlon shuts the book with a triumphant slap of his hand and shoves it in his school case. He kicks the case underneath the table as if it's a brak with leather ears. And away we go.

ONE AFTERNOON, WE'RE playing football in the street. Bruno and some of the dogs are there too, playfully chasing each other, barking and panting. Suddenly a brown 1957 Volvo, big and round and out of fashion, appears from nowhere and slams into Bruno. The dog flies into the air and lands back in the street with a horrible thud, sending up a cloud of dust.

A frightening moan comes from Bruno's throat. The car stops. A man gets out and says, 'What does the dog want in the street?' But immediately afterwards he says he's sorry.

We stop our game and form a circle around the dying Bruno. Blood from his mouth and one eye is trickling into the street.

He gazes at his master and dies. Derek sinks down on his knees by his dog and strokes him and starts to sob. Me and Peter and Marlon and Conos and Toolbag and everybody – two teams of six a side – all come and take turns putting our arms around my brother's shoulders. I put my arms around him the longest because I'm his brother. I whisper to him:

'Don't worry, don't worry.' I wish I knew more comforting things to say, but right now I can't think of any. There's a lot of death in the books that I read, a parent or brother or sister or sometimes even a horse. I usually read those parts more slowly because they're sad. But now that I need the words that they use to comfort the bereaved, I can't think of them.

'Don't worry.'

Derek doesn't look up at any of us and we can all hear the snot and the sobbing.

The man gets back into his car and drives away slowly. If he had driven like that in the first place Bruno would not be dead.

People come to see what the commotion is all about – other boys, girls and housekeepers. Agnes also comes to look and she says, 'Hayi! Nkosi yami,' which means 'Oh God!'

It's three o'clock in the afternoon and most of the mothers and fathers are at work. They'll hear about this tonight.

The flies don't waste time with something like this. A whole bunch of them are already buzzing around Bruno's nose and loitering on the drying blood.

We drag Bruno into our backyard to a spot in the shade of our kaalgat peach tree. Nobody actually says, this is where his grave will be, but we all just know it. I think we've chosen this spot because, in the cowboy movies, a grave is always in the shade of some tree, never just out there in the sun. It's sort of an address: after the funeral you can say, 'We buried him there by the peach tree' instead of just, 'We buried him there in the ground.' As we start digging in the hot summer sun I realise there's another reason – so that the gravediggers can have some shade while they're digging.

Toolbag is sweating so much from the digging, he says, 'By rights it's six feet for humans, three feet for dogs.'

For the last week or so, 'By rights' is his new way of starting sentences. He wipes his sweat off his face with the collar of his yellow T-shirt and says, without blinking, 'Council regulations.'

Jerome says, 'You making it up, don't think I'm stupid, you making it up.'

I can see an argument starting so I point to the dead Bruno and say, 'Gents, where's your respect?'

We end up putting Bruno in a hole about four feet deep.

Peter says, 'Gents, let's pray.' I glance at Derek to see if he's OK with it, but his eyes are closed already. (He has at least stopped crying and there are two streaks of dry tears over his freckles.) We hold hands and Peter prays:

'On behalf of all of us and our dogs Oortjies and Jacko and Boer, we ask God to accept Bruno as one of his main dogs. Amen.'

As we're closing the hole, Toolbag again puts his arm around Derek and says, 'Watch what helluva big peaches you get on this tree next summer.'

When we get back to our football game, Derek gets a free kick – plus the opposition allows him to score an easy goal and we all shout, 'Derek, the man!'

When Ma arrives home from work, she already knows – courtesy of an eight-year-old spy-bek called Tessa Wilson. Tessa's been in every house in Flinders Street, knows every family member's name and sniffs out everybody's business.

She's a stringy girl with two frizzy ponytails that jiggle as she tells her skinder stories. Their housekeeper, Beauty, washes her every afternoon, smears her face with Vaseline and brushes her hair into those ponytails – but they pull her hair too far back from her forehead and leave her eyes wide open. This gives her stories greater dramatic effect.

Every afternoon at half past four Tessa makes her way to the bus stop at the corner of Avon and Colorado where she waits for her ma so that she can carry her handbag home and look important.

Every day she has a story for at least one woman that gets off the bus. And this day it was Ma's turn:

'Auntie Shirley, Bruno's dead and Derek and Crowbar and them had a funeral for him.'

So when Ma comes home she sinks into an armchair in the lounge (instead of the usual hard upright kitchen chair). In the armchair she seems swallowed up and tired.

Shaune and Alison have also come for the inquest. Shaune looks sad sitting on the couch – his dimples are shallow and his two bare feet are dusty. Alison is holding Ma's slippers, one in each hand, waiting for a sign to slip them onto Ma's feet. My little sister is a girl version of Derek with her wavy brown hair and her splash of freckles around her nose and her look of anxious intensity. From time to time she takes a deep breath to show her sympathy for Derek.

Ma asks, 'What happened here today?'

We tell her and she listens, shutting her eyes at the point where Bruno gets knocked.

'Where was Agnes?'

'Ironing or something. She came to look but she went back in afterwards.'

'And what's this about a funeral?'

'Ma we just buried the dog! What were we supposed to do? That Tessa must learn to mind her own business!'

Ma tells Derek, 'Come stand here by me.' With her fingers she fixes the parting in his hair, smooths down wayward strands, all the time calling him boykie and promising another dog soon. She also says, 'Bruno saved somebody's life today – if he wasn't there, one of yous could've been knocked down, am I right or wrong?'

Dad is working overtime so he'll be home late and will only hear the story when we're all fast asleep.

That night after supper there's far more scraps than usual – mostly from Derek's plate.

Cowboys and crooks with the sheriff

Sometimes I come home late in the afternoon – from playing in the streets – and the kitchen is full of delicious smells because Ma's cooking supper. I'm so hungry I could eat two plates of food, leave a pile of scraps for the dog and eat that too.

I hang around the kitchen and get in Ma's way. She says:

'The food will be ready soon.'

This means 'Go away', but I stay.

'What's for supper?' I ask Ma.

'Hurse met lang ore,' Ma replies. (Hurse with long ears.)

There's no such creature as a hurse with long ears, in Africa or the world. But if there were I would like to nibble on its long ears while I wait for Ma to serve up the rest of it.

My favourite food is chicken curry. If Ma's cooking it you can smell it from a mile away. I know when Ma's going to make curry because of the pestle and stamper. The pestle is a thick shiny brass pot. The stamper is a shiny brass club.

Into the pestle go a piece of ginger, some garlic and a chilli. Ma goes into the backyard and, with the stamper, stamps what's in the pot. While she stamps she doesn't look at what she's doing; averting her eyes because a chilli pip doesn't like being stamped – it gets so angry that it leaps out of the pestle and into the nearest eye.

As Ma stamps away, it makes a dull sound that echoes against the minedump – like a bell announcing to the world that we're having curry for supper.

Sometimes on summer afternoons Derek and I play football on the football field down the street. The games are rough and tough and full of hard knocks and hard curses.

Then suddenly the afternoon changes colour – a pale yellow as the sun sinks slowly down behind the minedump. Into this yellow the smoke from hundreds of chimneys curl their charcoal patterns.

The game doesn't stop abruptly, it dies out slowly as one by one the boys walk off the field and go home.

Derek and I make our way up Flinders Street and breathe in the smells from everyone's kitchens – it's like walking down a path of lovely smells – curry, bredie, fried boerewors, tomato gravy…

When we get a whiff of the curry, I turn to Derek and say, 'Please, please, please, let that be from our house!'

Of course most times it's not. But when it is, I'm happy.

The curry is tasty enough already with the combined flavours of garlic, ginger and chillies. But Ma goes a step further: just as the curry is simmering in the pot, she cuts up some dhunia and sprinkles it on top. When you get a whiff of that, the inside walls of your cheeks turn to liquid.

The main ingredient of curry is of course curry powder. It's red, and red stands for danger. Ma keeps her curry in a bottle – but not an ordinary bottle. This one's got a glass lid and a brass ring to secure the lid. The curry is like a rare chemical that has to be hidden far away from the evil or careless amongst us who may use it to destroy the world. The curry powder also has its own teaspoon, a plastic one that stays in the bottle, half buried like a spade in a heap of red earth.

Every mother buys her curry from the Indian ladies in Diagonal Street. Sometimes an aunt or a neighbour goes on holiday to Durban and she always brings back some curry. It is claimed, by women who know their curries, that this curry is different from the Diagonal Street variety.

'Sometimes, when the devil runs out of fire,' it is said, 'he imports just one half kilo of mother-in-law curry from Durban.'

One day an aunt drops off half a packet of this notorious mother-in-law. Ma opens the packet and invites us all to come and have a look.

'It's so red it's almost maroon,' Dad says.

We laugh, but just a little, not wanting to offend the curry.

One night Ma uses the mother-in-law to make my favourite chicken curry. Will I be able to eat it, I wonder. I take a tentative forkful of food, chew, swallow, a glass of water by my side in case I burst into flames. And it tastes like any old curry.

The local shop sells Cartwright's Curry Powder. This is not real curry. It comes in a dainty little yellow and red box and looks more like a packet of sweets than real curry. On the box it says: 'English curry'.

Ma says there's no such thing as English curry. She says next thing they'll be selling English boerewors. But she says this Cartwright's is just right for making sugar bean curry and for flavouring pickled fish.

The other thing that goes into curry is elachi. It's a pip the size of a cockroach. Like the ginger and chillis, it's used for flavouring, but watch out – bite on the elachi itself and you don't want to go on eating.

You're happily eating away, rice, gravy, potatoes, a juicy chunk of curried lamb. And suddenly your jaw freezes. You pull a face and you go, 'Gahhh!' You've bitten into elachi.

That's why we call them speed traps.

EVERYBODY HAS SOMETHING they don't like to eat. Cabbage is not my favourite. Ma makes it in a bredie – I push my plate to one side. Ma tries a kind of curry with it, but I still don't like it. Then there's a third option that I find a big waste of time. Ma makes frikkadels and wraps each one in a cabbage leaf – mama in die kombers – mama in the blanket. Why? Is mama getting cold? I take off the blanket and put it in a pile on the side of my plate where I keep all the stuff I've discarded; cinnamon sticks, the husk of a squash. If I've got some time to kill I dump the cinnamon sticks in the husk and wrap it all up in the blanket.

I don't know anyone who doesn't like cowboys and crooks. Ma cooks it in winter, but I'm sure I could eat it any time from January to Christmas Eve.

Ma cooks up sugar beans (the cowboys) and samp mealies (the crooks). Actually, now that I think about it, I don't really know which are the cowboys and which the crooks. Also into that pot go soup bones. Ma dishes it up in bowls with the bones submerged in cowboys, crooks and a thick gravy.

Around the dinner table there's a whole lot of sucking going on until those poor bones are white and dry.

Oh, and if you're going to have cowboys and crooks, make sure you have some Wooster sauce (Worcestershire sauce). It's so good for samp and beans that it deserves a special name of its own – let's call it the sheriff – responsible for keeping law and order amongst those cowboys and crooks.

And what about skinderbek kos (gossipmonger food). Now there's a meal with a story.

Ma worked all her life. But there were times when she was at home – either when she had a baby or when she was looking for a new job.

Then, sometimes when I'd come from school in the afternoon, I'd find Auntie Maureen at home visiting Ma.

I don't have to be a detective to see that Ma's friend has been here for hours: sticky tea cups on the table, my baby sister's nappies soaking in a basin instead of hanging on the line, stompies in the ashtrays.

Auntie Maureen lives a street away. She and Ma go way back to when they were teenagers and played hockey together. Now they're married and have babies and older children who come from a hard day at school and are hungry.

'Ag you can make your own lunch,' Ma says. 'Look at what a big boy he is, Maureen.'

It's just flattery so that I can go away and take care of myself. I cut two slices of bread – uneven doorstoppers, but I'm too hungry to mind. I smear one slice with butter and the other with apricot jam while I listen to the two friends in the lounge giggling and laughing about old times and about the neighbours. This is when I realise how my ma likes to start her sentences with: 'At any rate...'

Ma and her friend are carrying on like drunk men, smoking cigarettes, leaving the house untidy and the children to see to themselves.

Every fifteen minutes or so Auntie Maureen says, 'Hey, let me get up and get out of here,' but she doesn't because they tell another story and have another cigarette.

And then suddenly it's half past four and Ma jumps up and says, 'Is that the time already? My God! And I haven't put the pots on!' Auntie Maureen runs away because she's got the same problem at her home.

Now Ma has to cook and supper has to be ready by six thirty because that's when Dad comes home. If it isn't ready he'll say, 'But what have you been doing all afternoon?'

What is Ma going to cook? Beef is out of the question. Ma hasn't got any. And even if she did have some, that meat takes a good few hours to get soft. Mutton is not such a tough customer, it only needs about an hour. But Ma hasn't got an hour.

The answer is mince!

'Chris, quick, go to the butcher, buy forty cents' mince...'

'Ma...'

'I don't have time for arguments, just go, run.' She shoves me out of the kitchen.

Twenty minutes later I'm back with the parcel of mince. In the kitchen I can hear the onions in the pot sizzling their song, 'Put in the mince, we want the mince!' Ma says they're braising. Then Ma goes into the yard to stamp up the garlic, ginger and chillies.

When my dad comes home from work, Ma dishes up mince curry and rice with potatoes in small cubes. Quick to cook, and as delicious as any other food. That's why they call it skinderbek kos.

My diary

The first thing I ever write in my diary is:

Today was my lucky day.

And this is why. One evening I go over to Marlon's after supper, for a chat and to see if he's got a couple of comics to lend me. We're sitting in the kitchen when his ma walks in from her bedroom.

'Here's a diary for you,' she tells Marlon and puts a blue hardcover book on the table in front of him. It's brand new and the paper is pure white and crispy. On the cover it says: 'DIARY – 1969'.

Marlon looks up at his ma, glances at me and sniffs at the diary. He looks puzzled, even a little irritated.

'What am I supposed to do with this?' he asks. He lifts up the cover with a contemptuous thumb, and drops it again as if it were the lid of a smelly dustbin.

'Write in it,' his ma says.

'Like what?'

'Your plans for the day, what you thought about the day, secrets.'

Marlon thinks about this for no more than three seconds (one second for 'plans', one for 'thoughts' and one for 'secrets') before he pushes the book away.

'Uh-uh,' he shakes his head. 'I don't have time for that.'

Auntie Gladys shakes her head too.

'You don't know how lucky you are to have that diary,' she says. And she explains to us how it found its way into her hands. Fifteen diaries were bought for the white staff at the accounting firm where she works in the mailroom. Three of the staff had already bought their own. The boss then offered the three spare diaries to the children of the white staff. But the school had supplied the students with diaries.

'What do I do with these then?'

'What about the people in the mailroom?' one of the accountants asked.

'What would they do with a diary?'

'The same thing you do with it.'

'Well let them have the diaries then, if they want them.'

The mailroom staff was made up of two coloureds – one of them Auntie Gladys – and two Africans. Dougie, the other coloured, was in the non-European toilet when the diaries were handed out. Auntie Gladys put the diary in her bag and brought it home on a dirty Putco bus to her 'ungrateful' son Marlon.

Auntie Gladys ends her sad tale with that heaving sound mothers make when they're disappointed in their children. She looks at me.

'Chris, would you like a diary?'

'Yes please, Auntie Gladys.' I take it and flip through it. It's so new that some of the pages refuse to come apart, but just for a moment.

And that's how, on 25 January, it becomes mine.

Writing in a diary, Marlon says, is for sissies. I don't agree. A boy can also own a diary as long as you don't say 'Dear Diary' every time you write in it and you don't dot your i's with little hearts.

When his ma leaves the kitchen, Marlon looks at me with disdain.

'You just took it to be nice to my ma,' he says.

'It's not true, I really want it.' I leave before he starts an argument with me – and without asking him for some comics. And the reason I believe this is my lucky day is because – just think about it – Crowbar could've been sitting there, or Toolbag or Derek.

(Well, actually, not Toolbag because that whole family is fast asleep at about eight thirty every night.)

It's the first time I've owned a diary and it's very interesting I must say. It's got helpful information such as Weights and Measurements. Let's say you're baking a cake and the recipe says: '12 oz of butter'. The diary shows you exactly how to convert that to grams.

The same goes for miles and yards. Let's say you find a treasure map under a rock on the beach. It says, 'The gold is buried underneath a tree 58 metres from here.' All you know about are yards, feet and inches. But not to worry: you take out your trusty diary and it shows you how to convert metres to yards. And in no time you've got your crate of gold coins and diamonds and rubies.

Marlon was really crazy not to take this diary. It's also got a list of all our public holidays. It's great to have a holiday, not to be at school, to wake up late and hang out with all the guys, play football or sit in the shade somewhere. But I don't want to write those things in the diary because they're just so boring.

Then I have an idea. I'll describe each holiday. And because that's boring too, I'll give my own version of it. Like this:

Van Riebeeck Day: 31 April
In 1652 Jan van Riebeeck, a Dutch sailor, arrived at the Cape in three ships, the Dromedaris, the Reiger and the Goede Hoop. I don't know in which ship he actually was. Van Riebeeck is regarded as the founder of the Cape and therefore of South Africa.

Dingaan's Day: 16 December
In 1804 the British came and took over the Cape from the Dutch. The British then abolished slavery.

The boers were so angry, they built a few hundred oxwagons and decided to leave the Cape, find a place to settle and start over.

There were no roads at the time so they rode over the Drakensberg mountains. This is why they called their journey the Great Trek.

They chose a leader called Piet Retief. Retief had been in jail for theft and became a good leader because, of all the people on the Great Trek, he wanted open spaces the most.

After a while the Voortrekkers came upon the Zulu chief Dingaan. Dingaan did not like white people on his land. He invited Retief for lunch so that they could talk things over rather than fight.

Retief and his friends went to Dingaan's house and rang the bell. Dingaan had a doorbell which, instead of going ding-dong like most bells, it went ding-gaan.

Retief and his Voortrekker friends laughed out loud and called it a silly thing. Now in Zulu culture you never laugh at a man's doorbell. Inside the house Dingaan heard them laughing and this made him so angry that he killed the whole lot of them.

Sometime later Retief's followers got even with Dingaan at the Battle of Blood River which they won on 16 December 1833. And that is why we have Dingaan's Day.

One day when Conos comes around I read my Dingaan story to him. When I come to the part about the bell that goes *ding-gaan,* he has a good chuckle.

I read it out to Agnes too. She stands in the doorway, listening, but ready to go as soon as it's over. When I get to my clever ding-gaan joke she shows no reaction.

'D'you know who Dingaan was?' I ask her.

'Yes, the boers kill him. But those days he didn't live in a house with a doorbell.'

'Agnes, it's a joke,' I tell her.

She shakes her head dismissively.

'Agnes…' Conos, who has been lying comfortably back on my bed, sits up to explain.

But Agnes swings around. 'I got eggs to lay, chickens to hatch,' she says, and heads for the kitchen.

'She's got *what?*' Conos asks me with a puzzled twitch of his nose.

'She always says that.'

Conos stares up at our ceiling. Then he turns to me. 'What would you do if the government read that?' he asks.

'Read what?' Although I know he's referring to my Dingaan joke.

'*Ding-gaan*,' he says, making the sound of the bell – it's as if he's taunting me with my own joke.

'Retief was one of their leaders and you're poking fun at him.'

'He was one of their leaders, ja, but he wasn't God!' I wish he'd at least sit up when he starts talking politics with me.

'Don't get angry with me, bra, I'm just telling you what the government might do.'

I wish Conos would just get up and go home and do his homework instead of lying here on my bed trying to scare me.

'Do you know what's a communist?' he asks.

'Sit up if you want to debate with me.'

'OK,' he says. He sits up and asks me again.

'A communist is an atheist and also someone who wants to kill everyone in his path.'

His thick eyebrows go upwards – he's impressed. He extends a hand.

I sneer at his hand, and then I sneer at him a little bit – and only then do I shake his hand.

'You know your stuff,' he says.

When Conos goes home, I lie on my bed thinking. My school tie is fifty per cent loose, my socks are on the floor, my shoes are in the way. Agnes comes into the bedroom and sees all this and says, 'Are you fighting with your friend again?'

'No,' I shake my head. 'I just put him in his place.'

But I'm not so sure if I did. I remember reading about a communist who was sentenced to life in prison. His name was Bram Fischer. According to the story in *The Star*, he and his friends had secret meetings and planned things. But the government found out what they were doing and now he's in jail.

The government put Bram Fischer in jail, and it's the same government that says apartheid is right. But I know apartheid is not right because my dad says it's not right. My dad says white people get all the nice things and we get all the scraps. 'Look at their houses compared to our little matchboxes,' my dad says.

And now I'm beginning to suspect that Bram Fischer was on our side.

But what is a communist? I get up and fetch my dictionary from my little bookshelf in the passage:

Communist. *Supporter of communism.*

'Thank you very much Mr Dictionary,' I mumble. Luckily I only have to move my fingers a few words up.

Communism. *The political theory or system in which all wealth and property is owned in a classless society by all the members of that community.*

How do you like that? Our Business Economics teacher told us once that if you want to borrow money from a bank you have to have money because the bank wants to make sure that you can pay the money back. It's the same with this dictionary of mine: you have to know words if you want to know words you don't know.

Now I will have to go and look up 'classless'. And when I find that, there will be another word I don't know, and so on and so on.

I don't need a dictionary to help me, I need a person, someone who knows about communism, knows a communist – or even someone who *is* a communist.

Sometimes I don't think I'll ever understand what's going on in this country.

A panoramic view

One afternoon I turn to Conos and say:

'I wanna ask you a question.'

'Ask.'

'Does this ever happen to you: you're doing your homework or you're listening to the radio or you're in class listening to a teacher and you hear a word for the first time, right?'

'Right,' he nods.

'Let's say the word is…,"perturb", right?'

'Right.'

'And then you suddenly hear – or see – that same word all over the place: on the radio, in a book, in a movie…'

He nods. It happens to him too although he can't, no matter how hard he thinks, give me an example.

'But you say it's just happened to you?' he asks.

'Ja.'

'And what's the word?'

'Panoramic.'

'Panoramic,' he tries the word too. 'What does it mean?'

'Do you know that you've experienced something "panoramic" already?'

'Is it?' He likes the way I'm dragging this out.

I nod. 'Hundreds of times.'

'Where? How?'

'Every time we climb to the top of the minedumps and look down on Riverlea we see the rows of houses that look like doll's houses, the churches, the cars, the tiny people in the backyards. That's a panoramic view.'

'A wide view of everything?'

'Ja, that's it!'

Conos and I sometimes have such interesting conversations that we forget where we are. For instance, we began the whole discussion about words and 'panorama' when we got off the bus in town.

Then we walked up to the Magistrate's Court in Marshall Street. We sat in the queue, Conos signed the form at the counter, the lady gave him the maintenance money – in cash – that his divorced father left there. We walked down to Kapitans in De Korte where we bought half a dozen curry balls and two Fantas to have on the bus (as we do every month).

We popped in at The French where Conos bought a pair of pantihose for his ma – size: large; colour: smokey.

We walked to the bus, stood in the queue for almost an hour, paid our fare, found a two-seater. I sat by the window because it was my turn.

During all that time we saw, smelt and heard the city.

We saw pedestrians, white people behind high counters, cars and trucks, high-rise buildings, Indian vendors in long bright floral saris.

Saw 'Whites only' signs on park benches.

We smelt the inside of the Magistrate's Court which was a mixture of oldness, wood polish and sweat.

We heard hooters blaring, people yelling, American jazz with its trumpets and drums and pianos.

But we didn't really see or smell or hear anything.

Maybe there's a word for this not seeing things that are right in front of you. And maybe it's the opposite of 'panoramic'. I don't know.

But actually – and I didn't want to tell Conos this – actually the word that I've been seeing a lot of these past few weeks is:

Communism

I have a secret, such a big secret that it makes me scared and it sort of excites me.

I am a communist. I can't tell my parents, my brothers and sisters, Agnes or Vino. I can't even tell my best friend Conos – the one person I tell everything.

I feel bad that I haven't told Conos. Especially since he told me a seriously big secret. He told me how his ma is worried that he's not growing as fast as other boys. She takes him to a doctor in town who makes him take off all his clothes and cough and get onto a scale.

'We go every Saturday for a check-up,' he told me softly – and then stopped talking when some girls walked past.

I don't know much about communism, but what I do know is this:

The whole of Russia is communist. We are supposed to hate the Russians because they are evil. I don't know what they do that's evil but it's so evil that we don't even talk about it.

The Russians call each other 'comrade' and they never make jokes.

I'm always making jokes, and I can't help laughing when Conos or Agnes or somebody on the radio makes a joke. But it's a good thing, I've decided; it's my cover. If I suddenly stopped laughing it would only take a few days for somebody to work it out and say: 'He doesn't laugh any more. Something's bothering him. Ah! Maybe he's a communist!'

Communists don't believe in God. I lie in bed at night and think about this. I'm not brave enough to follow this rule. What if I decided right now that I don't believe in God? A bolt of lightning could strike me dead right here in this bed. But why then don't we hear that all the Russians are being struck down one by one over there in Moscow.

I think of my friend Crowbar and an embarrassing church thing that happened to him year before last. Every Sunday he got dressed for church and Sunday School.

Crowbar's ma would give her son five cents for collection and another five cents for the Sunday school collection plate.

Crowbar always looked smart, walking down the street to church, greeting everybody along the way, a Bible and hymnal tucked under his arm. But he was not on his way to church! He went to the shop and bought a loose Rothmans cigarette and a packet of Cherrols sweets with the collection plate money.

Then he walked all the way up Colorado Drive and into the veld where there were broken down mining houses, their hideout – 'their' being Crowbar, Peter (before he was sent to boarding school), Marlon and a guy called Alexander, a tall, light-skinned guy with a pile of freckles around his nose who sniffed instead of laughed.

They smoked cigarettes and joked about how they were fooling their parents.

'Hey, listen!' Crowbar shushed them all. From far away, in the church where they should've been, they heard the holy boys and girls singing with gusto:

If you're happy and you know it clap your hands
(clap-clap)
If you're happy and you know it clap your hands
(clap-clap)
If you're happy and you know it
And you really wanna show it
If you're happy and you know it clap your hands.

Crowbar, in white shirt and crooked bowtie and Beatles fringe, blew a stream of smoke into the roofless room and broke into his own version:

If you're happy and you know it take a puff.

But, as they say, all good things must come to an end. Crowbar's ma found out where he was going on Sunday mornings. She fetched her Jesus belt hanging from a hook in the wardrobe – thick and long and guaranteed to teach lessons where the Bible and prayer had failed.

Crowbar was proud to show us his bum afterwards, two bluish hemispheres.

'Jislaaik!' we all cried out together.

'And that's only for not going to church,' Crowbar pointed out. 'The tannie doesn't even know about the cigarettes because I used to hide the smell with the Cherrols.'

That was quite something. But now, as I lie in my bed and think about communism, I wonder if the opposite of what happened to Crowbar is not perhaps happening somewhere in a Russian suburb far, far away.

Let's say there's a boy – we'll call him Crowbaski – leaving home right now.

'Where you off to, my little darlink?'

'I going to the veld, Ma, there to play with my comrades in old broken down house.'

'You have fun, darlink. Here is a rouble for cigarette.'

'Thank you, Mama!'

But Crowbaski doesn't go to the veld. Instead he makes his way to a house on the edge of the suburb where he attends a secret church service.

And then one day his ma finds out. She goes mad and says, 'You shame me! Every time you go you tell me you are going to veld to smoke cigarette with comrades! But where do you go? You go to a church and sing song about Jesus and pray and shout hallelujah.' And then she takes a belt and gives him a hiding.

SOMETIMES I FORGET that I'm a communist. Two or three days can go by without my remembering. And then suddenly I hear something on the radio and – wham – I'm a communist again.

One evening I'm sitting in the lounge with Ma and Dad, Derek and Shaune. We're all quiet because Dad and Ma are listening to the news on Springbok Radio. I'm listening too although most of the stuff the newsreader tells us about I just do not understand.

Why are the Americans fighting a war in Vietnam? It's got something to do with communists, but I don't know what.

Where is Biafra? They show pictures in the papers about people in Biafra, and it seems like everybody's starving to death.

Why is there a war on the border? Where is the border? It seems like our army is stopping communists from getting into our country and taking over. Every Saturday there's a programme on the radio called *Forces Favourites* – girlfriends write in requesting their boyfriends' favourite song – all white people. There's always a message, like: 'We're keeping the beer cold' or something like that. And there's always: 'Only three more weeks to go before we're together again.' And the presenter always says, 'Vasbyt, min dae' before she plays their favourite pop tune.

Then the Prime Minister, John Vorster, speaks. He says: 'The communists will never take over this country because we have God on our side…'

He has a sad voice with no sense of humour. He sounds like a man who has never been a boy, never played a prank, never held a frog in his hands, never liked a girl, never shared a secret with a best friend. He sounds as if he were born to warn others about the communists.

Another thing the Prime Minister likes talking about is 'The Coloured Problem'. What is this coloured problem, I ask myself. Why are we a problem to him?

One afternoon I turn to Agnes taking washing off the line, and ask her: 'What is the coloured problem?'

'The what?' she asks me, slipping a finger under her beret and scratching her head.

'The coloured problem.'

She thinks for a while, says she doesn't know what I am talking about, and goes on with her work. But later on, she comes to me and says, 'I know the answer.'

'Tell me.'

'When coloureds drink too much they break each other's windows.'

We both laugh. There have been a few incidents lately at a certain home down the road.

'And the Zulu problem, Agnes?'

'No problem,' she says without even thinking about it. 'We are Number One.'

But tonight, on the radio, it is the turn of the communists. I don't understand what the Prime Minister is saying, but I sit on the couch and listen anyway. Dad is punctuating the Prime Minister's words with those *mhm mhm mhm* grunts that could mean 'I'm impressed' or 'I don't know what the hell you're talking about but if I go *mhm mhm mhm* my wife and kids will think I do'.

While I listen, I watch Dad, Shaune who's watching Dad's Gold Dollar smoke curl towards the ceiling, Ma who has come in to listen with a dishcloth in her hands, and Derek who's rearranging a doily on the table. I look at all of them and think, 'Poor people, you have a communist sitting right here amongst you and you don't even know it!' And I shake my head.

I was a communist for a few months when I resigned. Well, actually I suppose I just stopped being one – about the time when I spoke to someone who knew someone who had actually known a real communist.

Someone who knew someone

I'M doing my Geography homework at the dining room table. Agnes is orbiting around me with a cloth, dusting the armchairs, the dining room table, the sideboard, the window sill. She also dusts the long Pilot radio – but is careful not to go near the knobs and buttons.

This is because the radio is on Radio Zulu and Agnes is listening to her daily serial. And for fifteen minutes, from three to quarter past, Agnes and I say nothing to each other, not a word. Not even a smile passes between us.

And when listening to this serial, it seems, there is nothing to smile about. I don't know isiZulu but the emotions come through loud and clear. There is a lot of slamming of doors and arguing. Explaining. Sobbing. Warning.

I watch Agnes as she listens. She buffs and buffs and buffs the table. And then suddenly she stops – and listens. She clicks her tongue, she shakes her head, she sags into an armchair. She sighs, she shakes her head, she scratches a spot on her head underneath her beret.

And then the drama stops, the Sunlight soap commercial bursts out from the radio, a familiar baritone urges Agnes to listen again tomorrow. And I'm relieved because Agnes becomes Agnes once more and I can talk to her. Today I have something to ask her.

'Agnes.'

She turns to look at me.

'Sit.'

'I've got eggs to lay and…'

'Chickens to hatch,' I complete her slogan. 'OK, don't sit then. Just tell me, do you know Lilian Ngoyi.'

'Of course!' she says proudly.

'What kind of woman is she?'

'Not scared of the boers. She walk straight in front in the march, that Lilian.'

'Was she a communist?'

'A what?'

'A communist.'

'I don't know about those things. Is that in your schoolbook?'

'No, we don't learn about those things at school.'

But she's not listening any more and has disappeared into the kitchen.

I go back to the universe, to the sun and the Earth that revolves around it.

She pops up again in the doorway.

'Your friend with the glasses, the tall one, what's his name?'

'Huh? Peter.'

'What's Peter's mother's name?'

'Auntie Sophie.'

'That one she was a friend of Lilian Ngoyi.'

Then she's gone again, leaving me smiling at the spot where she stood.

AUNTIE SOPHIE IS Peter's ma and they live three streets away in Ganges Street. Auntie Sophie is a shop steward in a clothing factory. Whenever I go and visit Peter, I hear Auntie Sophie talking about what a bad thing apartheid is. Very few other people in Riverlea say this about apartheid – either because they are scared of the police or they simply don't care.

And how does Agnes know about Auntie Sophie and Ngoyi being friends? Auntie Sophie is the only coloured I know who can speak isiZulu, and she must have told Agnes, one day, for some reason, that she knows Ngoyi.

Peter's pa died in a car accident a long time ago before they moved to Riverlea.

Peter stayed in Ganges with his ma and his two older sisters. I say 'stayed' because, for a while now, he has been at a boarding school in Ixopo in Natal.

He wrote me only one letter, complaining about the nuns who, whenever they were cross, called him and his schoolmates 'You natives!'

That very afternoon, when Auntie Sophie is home from work, I go to visit her. She's sitting at her kitchen table drinking a cup of tea, the pots are dancing nicely on the stove and good food smells are coming from them. And she seems pleased to see me. So all this gives me courage to come out with my question straight away.

'Auntie Sophie, are you a communist?'

Auntie Sophie lets out not a feminine chuckle but a big loud masculine guffaw that sends tea spurting from her mouth. 'Hoor wat vra die kind my nou?' she blurts out.

She tells me to sit down 'there' at the other end of the table. This means that I will be given a long answer, and that's what I want.

She takes off her glasses and wipes them clean with the cuff of her blouse. Her eyebrows are high like Peter's and her hair, streaked with grey, is combed back into a bun.

'When I first went to work at Weinberg and Sons,' she says, 'I was eighteen years old.' After a pause she says it again. 'Eighteen years old.'

'When was that, Auntie Sophie?'

'Nineteen fifty.'

I quickly work out in my head that she was born in 1932.

'Now you know what year I was born.'

I make another mental note to watch what I say or do in this kitchen. This woman is sharp; maybe you have to be sharp to be a shop steward – or a communist.

'Someone told me there were jobs for dressmakers. I'll never forget the dress I wore. It was a dark blue knee-length that came down to my knees.'

If it was a knee-length then obviously it came down to her knees, I'm thinking. But I don't say anything to her.

'Mr Weinberg interviews me and tells me, "You got the job." But, he says, "There is one problem."'

'What problem, Mr Weinberg?

"We already have a Sophie, so there will be confusion – if I call, 'Sophie' you will both come."

'Then this old man starts laughing and I realised he was making a joke and I started laughing too. Then he says: "Ah, I have an idea: We call the other girl Sophie, we call you Sophie Blue…"'

'Because of that blue dress you were wearing!'

'Because of that blue dress I was wearing.'

It seems like this story's going to take a long time. But I don't really mind – there's lots of interesting stories on the way to the end.

Auntie Sophie interrupts her story to call her daughter to the kitchen, 'Bernadette!' – and when she appears – 'The potatoes.'

Bernadette peels potatoes and cuts them into quarters. Bernadette is in training, to cook supper every day.

All over Riverlea, girls are cooking supper and I think about my ma. Every evening she comes from work and cooks our dinner, but sometimes when it gets too much for her, she says, 'My three eldest are all boys who can't even peel a potato!'

Bernadette is about three years older than me. Standard Eight is keeping her busy and opened books are spread out on the dining room table. She seems amused that little me is here interviewing her ma.

'Is this for a History assignment?' she wants to know.

'Guh!' Auntie Sophie spurts again. 'Communism a school project! That will be the day.'

Pots all sorted out, Auntie Sophie returns to her story and tells me about a communist called Solly Sachs and what happened once.

'In the 1950s, Solly was the president of the Garment Workers' Union. Imagine that! This white man, in the middle of apartheid, fighting for the rights of hundreds of coloured and African women working in factories all over Joburg.'

'What rights, Auntie Sophie?'

'Better wages, better canteens, proper lunch breaks, proper tea breaks, maternity leave, bonus.'

She gives me a chance to absorb all this.

'If you don't fight for these things the bosses don't just give them to you on a tray.'

'It's true, Auntie Sophie.'

'Imagine: a white man fighting white men for black women. Ask your mother, she's also a factory worker, she knows Solly Sachs.'

'I'll ask her, Auntie Sophie.' I wish I hadn't asked about rights because Sophie Blue is getting cross. But she calms down a little, and says:

'You know what Solly Sachs did once?'

I don't even want to guess.

'It was his birthday and he was coming to visit our factory on that very day. And the girls at Weinberg and Sons collected some money – five bob from each girl – and bought him a present – a dozen silk shirts!'

'Did he like his present?'

She holds her hand up; it means I should be quiet and listen.

'After we had our trade union meeting, we take him into the canteen. There's a cake waiting and we – all the girls – we sing happy birthday, cut the cake, tea – and we ask him to open his present. It's a long, flat box. He looks shocked. He says not a word, just opens it. And then he takes out all these shirts, a blue one, a yellow one, a beige one…'

'So what did he say, Auntie Sophie?'

'What did he say? He exploded with anger and started shouting at us: "What the hell do you women think you're doing! Expensive silk shirts for me! From workers who are so poor they – you can hardly feed your families!"'

That was the story of a real communist.

A Russel at the gate

It's a Monday afternoon. I'm sitting at the dining room table doing my homework and minding my own business – well you can say I'm minding the business of the whole of Europe in the Second World War, because that's what my History assignment is all about.

'Chris!' somebody shouts from the street. I put the music softer – my new Black Sabbath LP called *Changes*.

'Chris!'

That is not a voice I know. I open the front door, and standing there at our front gate is none other than Russel Harris. I'm in trouble, I'm sure I'm in trouble.

Russel is in matric. He's not a prefect, he's higher than a prefect. He's a rebel. He smokes and drinks and he's forever walking with one of the prettiest girls in the school. I don't know what he says to them as they walk side by side from school, but they're forever giggling and saying things like, 'No, no, *no*.'

Russel is the captain of the Riverlea High senior soccer side.

'Howzit, Chris!'

I didn't even know that he knew I existed, never mind knew my name.

He leans over our front gate. He's wearing a T-shirt with 'Fruit of the Loom' on the left pocket, faded blue jeans and running shoes.

'Can I see you for a minute,' he gestures.

He seems amused at the surprise on my face, and as I walk towards him I try to be cool.

I can't say 'Heita' because he's older than me. Instead I offer an uncertain, 'Hi.'

'You OK?'

My 'hi' was obviously too uncertain. 'Ja.'

'You doing homework?'

'Ja, History.'

'I want you to do me a favour,' he says, and then he turns sideways and looks far away down the street as if there's something interesting going on down there.

'What?' I think I know what this is all about: three doors down from us lives the gorgeous Veronica McKay, in Standard Nine, and every matric boy's dream. On their gate, right next to the 'Beware of the Dog' sign is a sign that says: 'No Boys Allowed'. It was put there by Veronica's dad. It's invisible, but it's very clear to all the bigger boys in Riverlea. It's also luminous so that it can be read at night too.

I can go into that house any time I like because, I suppose, I used to go there before Veronica became sexy. Before she became quiet and walked straight up and stopped running down Flinders in her bare feet. Before she started splashing a drop of her ma's Body Mist under each arm every time she went to the shops. Before she began to carry a tissue under the sleeve of her jersey.

Russel Harris, I suspect, wants me to go into the McKay house and bring Veronica out – or give her a message. All he needs is to say the word and I'll do it for him with pleasure!

He's got a foolscap page rolled into a tube and he blows into it a few times. I wait. And when he eventually makes up his mind to tell me why he's here to see me, it's got nothing at all to do with Veronica – it's much more exciting!

'I'm here to see the Number One essay writer,' he says.

The compliment makes my face go hot.

'Am I right or wrong?'

I pull a face.

'Remember two weeks ago…you came into our class and you read that one that you wrote about…'

'The advantages of reading comic books.'

'Eish!' he says, and gives me a tap on the head with his foolscap pipe. 'That's the one! About Spiderman and those guys.'

'Ja.' Mr Garson took me on parade, having me read it out loud to the Standard Eight, Nine and Ten classes.

'Uhm…' he looks down the road and blows his paper bugle. 'I want you to write me an essay.' He looks at me.

'What for?'

'For school, for Canopy.'

Canopy is Mr Williams, the senior English teacher. He's got a degree in English from Unisa and is very well spoken. Whenever the white school inspectors come inspecting at our school, the principal asks Canopy to lead us in prayer in school assembly. Canopy always starts his prayer with, 'Dear Lord, under this canopy of learning we turn to you today…'

'What you say?'

'I'll do it.'

'Hey!' he says, as if I've just taken his schoolbag off his shoulders.

Now it's my turn to look down the road – the other end – to see if Conos or Vino are coming. If I tell them afterwards who was here and what he wanted they might not believe me.

'When do you want it?'

'It has to be in next Tuesday morning.' He looks anxious again. 'I would have given it a go but I've got an offer to go fishing with some buddies of mine – at the Hartbeespoort Dam.'

'OK,' I nod.

'But you haven't even asked what the topic is.'

'What's the topic?'

He hands me his paper bugle. I unfurl it. There, in his neat matric script of light blue ink that leans to the right, are the three topics:

The greatest movie I've ever seen
The dangers of alcohol
On a planet far, far away

'Which one do you prefer?'

He laughs at my cockiness and because the tube is out of his hands he gives me a friendly jab on the chest instead of a knock on the head.

'Anyone is OK.'

'Right.'

Where the hell is Conos? If he doesn't come around that corner right now he won't see me with Russel Harris. He will believe me, no doubt about that, but still, I really would like him or Vino to actually see me with Russel.

'So you'll have it ready when?'

'Next Monday afternoon – you can copy it down in your own handwriting Monday evening and hand it in Tuesday.'

'Sharp,' he says and gives me the thumbs up.

I give him the exact same greeting back.

On the Monday afternoon, when Russel Harris comes for his essay, I make sure Vino and Conos are there to witness it – and I even tell Agnes, whom I have told about the essay-writing deal, to watch through the window. Vino and Conos stand in the background while I do the handover at the gate. Vino has one foot against the wall of our house, Conos has one of his feet on a step. Even though they're watching what's going on at the gate, they're trying hard to pretend that they're not interested. It looks like we're a rock band and we're about to take a photo for an LP cover.

Russel takes a puff on a cigarette and unfolds the page.

'I've chosen the alcohol one.'

'OK, that's cool.' Before he starts reading he offers me a cigarette.

'No!'

'You don't smoke?'

'My toppie will kill me.' I shake my head. (I have had the occasional puff up to now, but I'll start smoking for real in about a week's time.)

'I wish I was you,' he says. 'I'm trying to give up.'

143

He reads the first few lines.

'What's buoyant?'

I tell him.

'OK, nice. I'll read it at home. Thanks, bra.' He walks down the street sort of buoyantly.

I CAN'T WAIT to hear what mark he gets for that essay.

'What you always get,' Vino assures me. 'No less than seventy per cent or more.'

'For sure,' Conos agrees.

'But remember, guys, this is for matric – and Canopy's doing the marking.'

Later, Agnes asks, 'Did he pay you?'

'For writing the essay, no.'

'He must pay you.'

'Why, Agnes?'

'It was a job. When you were writing it for him, he was fishing in the sea.'

'In a dam.'

The wait begins. Wednesday, Thursday, Friday. It must surely be Friday. But my new friend Russel spots me on the playground and says, 'He hasn't given us our marks yet.'

I groan. 'Has he also gone to Hartbeespoort Dam?'

'Huh?'

'Has Mr Williams…'

'I get it!' he chuckles.

The following Wednesday comes. We're changing periods, which happens every thirty-five minutes: we go there and they go here and for a full three minutes there's a noisy stream up and down the corridors.

Someone grabs me by my blazer sleeve. It's Russel!

'Howzit,' he whispers, and I can smell that he hasn't managed to give up smoking yet.

'We got our marks,' he says.

I've asked him so often that now I just wait to hear.

'I got nought.'

'Hey! Move it!' We both hear Mr van Rensburg's voice. 'Keep left, keep moving and keep quiet!'

'Nought!'

'I'll explain break.'

'NOUGHT!' VINO SAYS.

'That's what he said.'

When I see Russel at break he explains what happened. He really did get a big fat nought, but the news is good news for me – beyond my wildest dreams.

'I got a hiding for it,' Russel says.

'A hiding for it?'

He nods and offers me a slice of his sandwich – pilchard and sliced tomato.

'You can't be serious.'

He has too much food in his mouth to talk so he uses sign language to indicate four cuts on the bum with a cane.

'Why?'

'Canopy says I copied the story word for word from some magazine or book.'

I'm stunned. I was hoping for a sixty per cent. But this? This is a thousand times more than I expected. I can't wait to tell Agnes and the guys.

'Did you copy it?'

'No.'

I want to add, 'The only one who copied it is you.' But I don't.

The dangers of alcohol

I didn't copy 'The dangers of alcohol' from anywhere, but I did get the idea from a book called *African Folk Tales*. And even how I came to be the proud owner of this book is itself an interesting tale.

The other day I went down to Humphrey Davis's house. He's a boy in my class who lives down in Gouritz Street right opposite the railway line.

The Davis family have to listen to the noise of the trains all day, starting from about four in the morning. When Humphrey talks it sounds like there's a train in his throat going *ketlang-ketlang* between his syllables. And when he's not saying anything you can hear a whistle coming and going.

Humphrey happens to be one of the fastest runners at Riverlea High despite being a little fat. He's also good at Maths and that's why I find myself at his house after school. He's offered to help me get some Maths into my head.

Their lounge is packed with stuff – bookshelves full of books, papers, documents, old photos, new photos, newspapers, fresh and white from the day before to yellow and crispy from the year before.

It's untidy, but I like it. There must be treasures underneath these piles just waiting to be uncovered. And, sure enough, it happens when Humphrey starts searching for a textbook that he swears he had yesterday. He digs through a pile and out pops, not the textbook he's misplaced, but *African Folk Tales*.

'D'you mind if I borrow this?' I ask him, flipping casually through the pages. It looks like a book that could keep me enthralled (that's a new word I've learnt) for a long time. There's a story called 'The girl who loved danger', there's 'Seven birds and seven boys' and lots more. And illustrations on almost every page: boys by a river, birds in flight, monkeys prancing around in trees, girls playing a game with stones.

In a situation like this, the idea is to sound so calm, almost disinterested. You show excitement and the potential lender starts believing that there must be something in that tattered old book of such great value that he had better hang on to it and read it himself after all.

'Ja, no problem,' he says, still searching for his textbook.

And that's how I came to be the proud owner of *African Folk Tales*. If I give it back it's just going to disappear underneath one of those piles again.

MOST OF THE books that I read are written by authors who live in England or America and are set in these countries. But every now and then I come across a story that takes place right here in Africa.

These African stories are different from the overseas ones. They always happen in rural villages where there are no phones, radios or tarred roads. Everywhere you look is bush and cattle grazing on some grassy slope. Proverbs spill out of the mouths of the old people all the time.

A man's hut leaks – there's a proverb about being too lazy to fix one's hut.

A woman doesn't pay attention while she brews beer and ends up with bitter beer – there's a proverb.

A man doesn't plant his grain in time and his family has nothing to eat for winter – there's a proverb.

Every man has three or four wives. This means that the children have several mothers and more sisters and brothers than I have cousins. Each mother lives in a different hut.

The children go around almost naked but for their loincloths. The stories are always set in summer so that I don't really know what these people wear in winter – a woollen loincloth maybe.

People drink out of gourds – big round pots with zigzag patterns on them – and eat out of big banana leaves. I suppose this is a good thing because then your ma doesn't have to buy those Adams stamps every week and still not have enough for a dinner service at the end of the year.

Everyone sleeps on a mat.

The villagers are always celebrating some or other event.

A baby is born – they eat drink and dance.

A couple gets married – eat, drink and dance.

Plant seed – eat, drink and dance.

Harvest the mealies – eat, drink and dance.

A boy gets circumcised – eat drink and dance.

Actually, many of the men in Riverlea (including my father) eat, drink and dance almost every weekend. They don't need a special event to sink a nip and two beers.

The thing I like most about village life is how all the fathers are never at home. They all work at the cattle-post minding the family's cattle. And the cattle-post is a whole day's walk away. So father comes home only every two weeks – and stays for only a day or two. I could live with that.

Everyone speaks to each other in formal English. It's always, 'Yes, Father', and 'No, Mother'.

So it was from reading this book that I got the idea for writing that story for Russel Harris. And it goes like this:

Caught

'Sipho!'

'Yes, Mother.'

My agemates Mandla, Jabu and I were playing by the riverbank when Mother called me to her side.

'I am here, Mother,' I said, stooping to enter the dark hut. (Why do we not make the entrances higher, I often wondered. Maybe then Grandmother would not be on her mat suffering from backache.)

'You have to go to your father today,' Mother said. 'And soon, so that you can be back before sunset.'

'Yes, Mother.'

Mother gave me a reed basket packed with food and drink for Father and I set off as the sun was rising from its sleeping mat in the east. As the sounds of the village grew more distant behind me, the noise of the forest grew louder. Birds chirping and twittering in the trees, monkeys yapping at me in their quick chatter, a stream giggling over pebbles.

I knew these paths like the lines on my fighting sticks. The journey would take me two hours. Or three if I lingered by a river, met friends along the way or had a nap in the shade of a tree. Mother and Father would both forbid these distractions if they knew about them.

By noon I had almost completed my journey and had only half an hour's walk to go. Because I had walked briskly and made good time, I decided to rest by a stream and have a drink of cool water.

I had something else that needed satisfying too—my curiosity. I unpacked the basket to see what gifts my three mothers had given Father.

From Wife One (my own mother): a handful of cashew nuts, a shawl for the cold nights and a bottle of mouthwash from the medicine man to ease father's toothache.

From Wife Two: two pairs of new woollen socks, a gourd of vanilla-flavoured yoghurt, salt, a bag of ginger biscuits, tobacco and a new pipe.

From Wife Three (Father's youngest and most recent wife): kola nut (imported from Nigeria), a flat pillow so that father might sleep more comfortably at night, two new underpants (size XXL), half a loaf of fruitcake and a gourd of marula beer so freshly brewed that a bubbly froth was dancing on its surface.

I put my nose close to the brew and breathed in. The bubbles jumped up at me playfully. Of all the gifts, the beer impressed me most. I longed for the fruitcake with my heart. But it is with my head that I wanted the beer. I had watched my father whenever he drank beer with his friends and, like magic, he always changed into someone else right before my eyes.

Whenever he sat down to drink his beer he was, as always, stern with me, but pleased that his friends were around him. They would sit in a circle on mats or on logs, talking about stock theft and the best cure for a sick cow.

Another two mouthfuls and it was as if all their stolen cattle had come back and there were no sick cows in all of Africa.

In another few mouthfuls even the knots in their loincloths were coming undone and they were making jokes about birds that might fly away.

What would the marula beer do to me, I wondered. Then slowly an idea began to take shape in my head.

There in the shade of the marula tree I knelt down and dug a small hole and carefully placed the gourd of beer in the hole. With stones and small rocks I secured it. Assured that it would not spill and that no creatures could reach the beer, I continued on my way.

When I reached the cattle-post I found Father closing the large wood and wire gate to the enclosure.

'I see that you are limping, Father,' I said.

'Yes,' he grunted, jabbing an angry finger at the bull that had delivered the kick to his buttocks.

'I wish I had been here to see that,' I muttered.

'Did you say something?' Father asked.

'Just cursing the bull that had injured you, Father.'

Father and I sat down on two flat stones. He asked about all the family back home, about mother as well as my two small mothers. Then he reached for the basket and looked eagerly inside it.

'The beer,' said Father. 'Where is the beer?'

'I poured it out, Father,' I said simply.

'You what?'

The moment had come to put the second part of my plan into action.

'It had gone bad, Father.'

'But how could you tell?'

'It smelled bad and there were things floating on its surface. I took it out of the basket before it could harm your other food.'

For a while Father was speechless. And even when a fly came to sit on his forehead he did not bother to swat it away.

'I am sorry, Father,' I said. 'I shall tell my young mother that her beer had gone bad…'

'No!' Father chided. 'Don't you dare tell her that, or your other two mothers.' He thought for a moment. 'In fact tell her that I had enjoyed the beer very much.'

'Yes, Father,' I said, and my heart shouted an English word that I had learnt from the missionaries: 'Hallelujah!'

On my way back home, I found the beer where I had left it, bubbling away. I sat in the shade and proceeded to drink up. As I gulped it down I began to understand why my father loved beer so much – and why he was so disappointed that I had not brought beer.

I almost felt sorry for my father – but only almost. And then I stopped almost feeling sorry for him because a bird in the tree made a joke and I laughed. And then the tree said something funny too.

I stumbled through the forest singing a song I had heard at my older sister's wedding. After I had sung it about a dozen times, I reached home. I went straight to my hut stumbled onto my sleeping mat and fell fast asleep.

'Wake up!' It was my mother, tugging at my arm.

I opened my eyes and sat up.

'Why didn't you tell me you were home? How is your father?'

'Hiya, mate. How ya doing, Sheila?'

Ma leaned back on her knees in bewilderment.

'What's wrong with you?' she cried. 'Why are you speaking like an Australian?'

Tony Polony

Apart from my Dingaan's Day entry, my diary turns out to be rather boring. For instance, it reads like this:

Monday 16: Got up to go to school. Didn't have clean socks so I slipped on a pair of Dad's. I must make sure to wash them when I come from school.

Wednesday 17. Played truant today. I did not finish Mr van Rooyen's Maths assignment. My bum is in no mood for that cane of his. I stayed at home with Agnes and finished the assignment. And then I also wrote a letter, to Mr van Rooyen, signed by Dad, in which I expressed 'my sincere apologies for keeping Christopher out of school today. He was feeling queasy and was expectorating'.

I throw in these jawbreakers because Van Rooyen is Afrikaans speaking and these big words really impress him.

So when I read my diary a week or so later, I find it a little boring. I also get scared because I realise how often I play truant and forge my father's signature. If I don't stop it somebody's going to find out sooner or later. Somebody other than Agnes, I mean, because she already knows but she doesn't say anything.

THEN, ONE EVENING after supper, Ma makes an announcement that is really going to get the pages of my diary fluttering with gossip.

'Uncle Tony's coming to stay by us.'

We're all in the kitchen when Ma breaks this news (except for Dad who is reading *The Star* in his bedroom because, I take it, he knows this news already). Derek, Shaune and I are doing homework, while Alison is drawing a picture of Ma with a purple crayon.

'Who, Ma?' Alison asks.

'Uncle Tony.'

Derek says, 'Tony Polony.' And, of course, Alison repeats it.

'Who's he, Ma?'

'He's Auntie Jenny's new boyfriend.'

'Ooh!' says Shaune. 'Do they kiss, Ma?'

Ma nods and smiles.

'Where's he from?'

'Cape Town.'

'Then why doesn't he just stay in Cape Town?' I ask.

'Why should he?'

'Because Cape Town is nice with Table Mountain and the sea and all that. Miss Abrahams told us.'

Ma laughs and says, 'Well you can ask him why he doesn't live in Cape Town when you meet him. And,' she changes her tone from playful to serious, 'we're going to have to make a few adjustments around here.'

We pause for a while in our tens and units and verbs and nouns and listen. The adjustments go something like this: Uncle Tony is going to sleep on the couch in the lounge/dining room. That means no listening to the radio too late. I don't complain because when *The World of Hammond Innes* comes on at a quarter past ten I'm supposed to be fast asleep anyway.

Ma's going to make space in our wardrobe for Uncle Tony's clothes.

'But it's already so packed, Ma,' I point out.

'I'll make a plan,' Ma says.

And his suitcase goes on top of our wardrobe, Ma says. And we're not to touch it, not ever. And there will be things in the bathroom; his own soap, his shaving stuff, facecloth, combs and brushes. Don't touch.

We're so cramped already. Ma and Dad have their room. Me, Derek, Shaune and Alison sleep in the other room. And I suspect Ma's getting another baby.

Our room is one big mess most of the time. Someone's forever looking for a shoe or a shirt or a sock. Pencils go missing, hidden sweets disappear from their secret places, someone uses somebody else's facecloth. If you're in the toilet or the bathroom (which is the same place) there's always a knock and a 'hurry up'. And now we're getting another person in here.

I don't think it's a good idea, but I can easily imagine what would happen to me if I dared to voice my opinion.

'Just who the hell do you think you are?' Dad would say. 'Shirley, did you hear what this one just said now, did you hear, Shirley?'

It would be like that Cassius Clay boxing match we heard on the radio the other day—when Clay beat up that Henry Cooper guy from England. But this would be a fight between Nick 'Vloek die kind' and Chris 'Word gevloek':

Ding!

'Seconds out, round number one! We expect another night of drama here as "Vloek die kind" circles "Word gevloek". Vloek die kind's wife, and Word gevloek's siblings all have their usual ringside seats, looking mostly anxious as they await another predictable outcome.

'Remember, the Queen's blerrie rules apply: Nick has to swear at Chris in as many languages as possible: English, Afrikaans, Zulu, Tswana and Sotho. Chris, however, is only allowed to utter the words, "Yes, Daddy" and "No, Daddy". And—ooh, look at Chris reeling! That one came from nowhere—a word usually reserved for mean dogs—and another in Zulu that Nick picked up at the factory and which he saved for this occasion...'

Ding!

'End of round one.'

I DO HAVE an idea why Uncle Tony will be moving in. It's for extra income. Every family around here, it seems, has to have an extra income: the Millers also have a boarder, a man called Doelie from Kimberley who rides a size twenty-eight bicycle with his back straight up. Mrs Wills makes vetkoek and mince by the dozen every evening and sells it at the factory where she works; Mr and Mrs Lang sell koeksisters on Sunday mornings; Mr Moore makes – and this might be hard to believe – dentures for people who can't afford to go to a real dentist. Mr Barnes runs a weekend barbershop business under a shady peach tree in his yard; Mr Rayners shows movies in his lounge. There are also shebeens, fahfee houses, and women who sell popcorn, sweets and ice blocks.

And now the Van Wyks are going to have a boarder.

One Sunday afternoon Uncle Tony arrives, with Auntie Jenny by his side. I'm always happy to see my aunt, who is a little fat, with thick clumps of dark hair that roll onto her forehead and over her ears. But today all my attention is on the man with the suitcase.

He doesn't have teenage pimples but you can see that he used to have lots of them. He's light skinned. He has frizzy brown hair that, if he doesn't cut it soon, will become an afro. He's a little on the fat side too, and he's not as tall as Dad.

This is all I manage to take in before I'm told to 'go play'.

But as the days pass, I learn more and more about him. Afrikaans is his home language. He speaks English too, but not very well, pausing every now and then to find the right word. Sometimes he just throws in the Afrikaans word if he can't find the English one quick enough.

'I've been in the printing…bedryf since I left school,' he says, when the word 'industry' eludes him. And, 'This Christmas I'm gonna miss my mother's kalkoen dinner.' (He can't find the word for 'turkey'.)

He calls me by my nickname from day one. 'Ou Kuller!' he says when I pass him in the kitchen or the lounge. 'How goes it with ou Kuller?' In the beginning he hasn't got anything more than that to say, but as the weeks pass, he adds on more and more things.

He's got his own toothpaste in the bathroom. We use Colgate, he uses Aquafresh. We always run out of Colgate, but he never runs out of his toothpaste. I'm tempted – I look at the still-fat tube of Aquafresh basking proudly in the first rays of the morning sun. Not a million smiles away, in a dark corner of the medicine chest, the remains of the Colgate tube, flattened and rolled up, its cap cleaned out, its little round top brushed clean with someone's bristles. I'm tempted to steal just a little squeeze of the Aqua, but I don't. I brush my teeth with a brush that has a memory of Colgate from the day before.

The sound of Agnes scrubbing tackies in the bathroom becomes a squishing Thursday afternoon routine. One day I chat to her while she's bent over the bath, scrubbing, rinsing, inspecting – scrubbing, rinsing, inspecting, until all the grass and tar and polish and industrial printer's ink are gone or at least faded.

'It's hard work, hey Agnes?' I shake my head, feeling sorry for her.

She looks up at me, sweating, too cross and tired to talk.

From this boarder, Agnes gets an extra rand a week – which, I suspect, she could happily do without if he took his tackies and went away.

One Monday afternoon I step into our backyard and stop dead in my tracks. Fluttering on the washline are strange clothes, in colours that our family never wears: next to a green and mustard T-shirt, the orange underpants are the funniest, drying in the sun next to my dad's plain white ones.

I call Derek and point them out.

Derek says in a cowboy drawl, 'Where dem strange onnies come from, boy?'

I curl my fingers into binoculars, put them to my eyes, step back and gaze at the onnies. 'From down South ah reckon.'

One afternoon after school, Agnes calls us, me, Shaune and Derek, to the lounge where she points to the empty vase on the dining room table.

'Look inside there,' she orders us.

Derek is the first to look, and spots what Agnes wants him to. He laughs.

'Whatsit?' I want to know.

'Bubblegum.'

Shaune and I have a peek too, and there, stuck to the base, is about ten cents' worth of chewed out Chappies – a week's supply for any township boy.

We think it's a bit of a joke, but not Agnes.

'Why you put bubblegum in the vase. Every day I'm cleaning bubblegum, every day you put again.'

'It's not me.'

'It's not me.'

'It's not me, it's Uncle Tony,' Dereks says. And he knows because he's seen the uncle from Cape Town spit it in there.

With a 'Sies!' Agnes turns on her heel.

This gum thing is an embarrassment and a dilemma for Ma and Dad. Uncle Tony chews his gum loudly – and all the time! Both Ma and Dad hate us chewing gum.

'How many times do I have to tell you to stop chewing like a cow!' Ma says.

Dad says: 'Spit it in the bin! Now!'

But Uncle Tony just goes on and on chewing his gum and nobody stops him. I could drop a hint, but I won't – this is something for the pages of my diary and I want to see how it's going to end.

It so happens one evening that Ma and I are the only ones in the lounge, listening to *Twenty-One* on the radio.

We hear the gate squeak open, the five or six footsteps stomping up the three steps. There's a tap on the door, it opens. And it's Tony Polony with his inky fingers, his lunchbox and his trademark chewing. He stops to say:

'Evening, Shirl. Ja ou Kuller.' And he's off to the kitchen where his food awaits in the warmer.

Paddy O'Byrne is saying to a contestant: 'For five points name five of the six wives of Henry the Eighth.'

The lounge is not quite as it was: there is the echo of gum chewing left behind by Uncle Tony. I can't help myself. I say:

'It's loud, hey Ma?'

'Is what loud?'

I ignore Ma and listen to the answer.

'Anne of Cleves, Catherine of Aragon…'

'Is *what* loud?'

'The radio, Ma.' My tone is a perfect example of respect for one's parents.

'Anne Boleyn, Jane Seymour…'

Ma gives me a withering look but I pretend not to notice.

UNCLE TONY HAS his meals at the kitchen table with Ma and Dad. We take our plates to the lounge where we listen to the radio while we eat. Or we eavesdrop on them in the kitchen.

Some evenings Uncle Tony comes home late – because after work he goes to visit Auntie Jenny.

Some Saturdays he wakes up with a hangover. To fix his head up for the weekend ahead, he eats scrambled eggs for breakfast. This is a luxury that we hardly ever have.

'Kuller,' he calls me, 'go and buy me eight eggs. And a packet of Stimorols.'

I run to the shops and buy the eggs and his gum. I come back, hand them to him with his change, and hang around, hoping for five cents. He offers me not even a cent. Every neighbour in Riverlea gives you something. Even Mrs Hall who's always sending us for 'half a loaf of well-baked bread' will give you a cent sometimes.

Ah well, I shrug. Maybe this tipping is not really a Cape Town custom.

He cracks the eggs into a pan, adding chopped onion, butter, pepper, salt, a chilli. And in no time the kitchen is filled with the most heavenly aroma.

I stick around, hoping he'll give me a spoonful, just to taste, but he does no such thing.

He eats his eggs with thick slices of buttered bread while he listens to the *Pip Freedman Show* on the radio.

Pip Freedman is a white comedian who for about seven minutes mimics an exuberant Cape coloured:

'Hullo, hullo, master en merrem, Gatiepie here beck from night school. Dat's why I'm only clever at night! My teacher she ask me to make a sentence wit de words "income tax". I tink a little bit and den I put up my hand. "I got one, merrem." "Yes, Gatiepie?" "I had a little dog, his name was Tax. I open de door and in come tax."'

These rapid-fire jokes about us are interspersed with canned laughter – which I assume is the laughter of white people.

After an ad break it's the turn of one Philemon Ngaka, a servile, not too bright African. He tells us, 'My wife Beauty, she work for the white madam. One day the madam she put the shicken in the oven and she say to Beauty, "Beauty, I go to hairdresser now. I want you to take the shicken out of the oven when the clock say three fifteen." Beauty she say, "Yes madam, I will take the shicken out when the clock say that." After four o'clock the madam she come home and she smell something is burning. Ooh, it's the shicken! The oven is still on and the shicken is burnt black black black. The madam is cross with Beauty. "Beauty why didn't you take the chicken out of the oven when the clock say three fifteen?" Beauty say, "Madam, I wait and wait, but the clock it don't say three fifteen, it only say, tick-tock-tick-tock."'

After Gatiepie and Philemon Ngaka, the *Pip Freedman Show* is over. There's no time to poke fun at a white South African.

Peter told me once that his ma Auntie Sophie, finds the *Pip Freedman Show* so insulting that she has even written a letter to the newspapers to complain.

'So your ma doesn't even laugh?' I asked.

'No,' he said. 'She turns it off!'

A family without a sense of humour, I thought at the time. But slowly (and I'm talking about months, not hours), I began to see Auntie Sophie's point.

Uncle Tony obviously doesn't find it offensive at all. I decide to impress him.

'He makes fun of African and coloured people.'

He looks up at me, his surprise at my remark dulled by last night's drinking. 'Yes,' he nods.

'Why doesn't he tease Afrikaners?'

'Why doesn't he tease Afrikaners?' he repeats. 'Let's see now – I don't know and Uncle Tony's got a babalaas.' He picks up the newspaper and turns to the horse-racing page muttering: 'Newmarket mhm…third race…OK, OK…hmmm…outsider …let's see…mhm.'

This means only one thing: that I should buzz off. But before I disappear he says, 'D'you know a joke about Afrikaners?'

'I do.'

'Let's hear it?'

'No.' And I go in search of Conos.

The coming of the Cape Coloured Corps

One evening Uncle Tony comes home from work bursting with news for Ma and Dad, but if I turn down the volume of the radio a bit I can get the news too. It goes like this:

'Our receptionist calls me into the office. There's a call for me. Nobody calls me at work. Who can it be? Maybe Jenny. I say hullo. And when the man says hullo back I know exactly who it is – Peter February! My best friend from high school. He's now a corporal in the army, the Cape Coloured Corps. The man is excited, the army is coming up to Joburg next week. They're on a recruitment drive and they're trying to get some Joburg coloureds to sign up.

'He doesn't know where I live but he hopes we can get together when they come up here. I ask him where they'll be staying. He tells me there's an army base up here but it's for white soldiers. So in the meantime, since they'll be here in the school holidays, they've got permission from Coloured Affairs to billet at Riverlea! (he bangs the table with the palm of his hand) High! (bangs it again) School! (and again).'

And then he told this Peter February that if he happens to be sleeping in classroom 5b, not to fire his rifle out of the window and towards the minedumps.

'Why?' February wants to know.

'Because you just might shoot me, man, I live right there within shooting range!'

AND SO, DURING the June holidays, the Cape Coloured Corps comes rolling into Riverlea. One minute the high school is a drab deserted place of prefabricated classrooms, the next minute there are jeeps everywhere, tents pitched all over the place, and muscular coloured men looking busy. All beneath the orange, white and blue South African flag fluttering proudly in the June breeze.

In no time half of Riverlea's boys have their fingers clamped all over the school fence, watching and calling out to the soldiers. It's a weird sight: children staring eagerly into a schoolyard! The soldiers are friendly and enjoying the attention, and every now and then they come over to answer our questions.

'How many bullets do you have in your gun?'

'How far can a gun shoot?'

'When can I join the army?'

'Were you ever in a war?'

There is another interest group, quieter than us boys but no less admiring – the older Riverlea girls. Suddenly, despite its being a weekday, girls are sauntering past the school in their Sunday best. Hair is permed and gelled and combed in three different styles in one day. No girl is going about in rollers any more and stockings are being worn on the legs and not on the head.

The Cape Coloured Corps has turned Riverlea upside down.

Then one Saturday afternoon Uncle Tony throws a party at our home for his old buddy Peter February and about five or six other soldiers, and of course Dad.

Brandy and beer flow in the lounge and in the kitchen Ma's frying chops and wors and cooking a pot of tomato gravy.

Conos is hanging out with me this evening because any boy who won't stick around in a house full of real soldiers is a fool. They send us to the shebeen to get them more brandy and Conos says to the shebeen owner, 'Hurry up, it's for the soldiers!' and the man actually does hurry up.

Ma gives us a chop each with some bread and gravy. We sit in the kitchen and eat and listen to them chatting and laughing in the lounge. A lot of the talk is about women – their girlfriends back home in Cape Town whom they miss.

'I miss my goose,' one says, which makes Conos and me explode with laughter because it's a funny name for one's girlfriend.

One of them comes into the kitchen to chat to us. He's dressed in tracksuit pants, a green vest and sandals despite the nippy June weather. His arms are packed with muscles and he's a little drunk.

Conos and I are doubly impressed because, quite frankly, we'd like to have muscles *and* get drunk someday soon.

'Excuse me, can I ask you a question?' Conos says. 'Why did you join the army?'

The soldier plants one foot on a chair. 'To protect my people from the communists.'

'Who are the communists?' I ask.

'They are the people who want our country. And,' he halts me from asking another question, 'they don't believe in God.' He nods smugly, swaying from side to side.

Conos says, 'How long do you have to train to get muscles like that?'

'Every day twenty-four hours a day.'

Except for today of course, because right now he's busy getting drunk in our lounge with Dad and Uncle Tony and Corporals January, February and September.

'Some coloured people hate the Cape Coloured Corps,' he says.

'Why?'

He sighs at the stupidity of these people. 'They call us sell-outs. They say we should be fighting the government…'

'Why the government?' I want to know.

'Because of apartheid.'

He tells me that they're here in Joburg on a recruitment drive.

'Come to the Union Stadium next week Saturday,' he tells us. 'We're putting on a show for the public.'

'What kinds of things are you going to do?'

'I can't give it away, but there will be helicopters, tanks…'

'What if the communists attack us tonight?'

He struggles a little to focus on me and my question. 'Whatchoo mean?'

'If they attack us tonight, you won't be able to get to your rifle in time.'

He shakes his head lots of times; he disagrees, he says, 'You wrong there, boeta.'

'Why so?'

'Because the commu—' a loud belch interrupts him – 'the communists are also having a party tonight.' He hands me his burnt stompie to put out somewhere.

His friends call him back to the lounge, but first he stands in the middle of the kitchen and tells us to punch him in the stomach as hard as we like.

Both Conos and I initially refuse but he insists.

I give him two or three of my best shots in his solar plexus, and so does Conos, but he doesn't flinch, just laughs and sways.

'Just come,' he says. 'You won't regret it.'

'You coming with us?' I ask Conos.

He says he won't be able to.

'Why not?'

Right there in the soldier's presence Conos whispers in my ear why he won't be able to go to the stadium with us. I nod; it's a secret. In fact, it's written in my diary.

BUT I'LL BE there for sure. Uncle Tony says I can go with him and I spend the next week wishing the days would fly.

Saturday morning dawns and Uncle Tony and I are off to the Union Stadium to watch the Cape Coloured Corps. There are no buses to the stadium and it's a half hour walk – mostly the same walk I take to my ouma's house in Coronation.

Uncle Tony and I begin our journey.

He's wearing a floral green and yellow shirt, a mustard cardigan and green slacks. For further protection against the wintry weather he also has on his light brown leather jacket. This morning I watched him rub a handful of Brylcreem into his afro and it sparkles in appreciation as we step out of Riverlea.

He looks smart and I'm beginning to get used to Auntie Jenny's colourful boyfriend.

Me, I'm sommer dressed in my light blue shirt. The collar was frayed, and I say *was* because Ma removed the collar, turned it around, sewed it back on and now it's as good as new. I'm also wearing my old grey school pants – and here too, Ma has worked her magic, loosened the turn-ups and brought them down about an inch. I like it when Ma has to do that because she sits there at the table with the needle and thread and says, 'My God, where is this child growing to – I took these turn-ups out three months ago!'

I have on my dark blue windbreaker. I got it over a year ago but only wear it on special occasions. The label reads: 'London Fog'. I like that. Whenever I put it on I read the label first. Then I imagine myself walking the streets of London, my collar turned up, a mysterious silhouette, and the Londoners saying: 'But who is that man?'

The Union Stadium is in Western Coloured Township.

'D'you know where it is?' I ask Uncle Tony.

'Ja,' he says. 'I've gone to watch a couple of rugby matches there.'

'Rugby?' This is news to me.

'Rugby,' he nods, and smiles. 'Very good games between Joburg teams and Cape Town and Port Elizabeth teams.'

I'm not interested in rugby and I didn't even know that coloureds played it. Sometimes I listen, with half an ear, to the commentary on the radio and all I hear is 'bloed' and 'trap' and 'skop'. The teams are always white and I get the feeling that the commentator, with his deep warlike bark is not talking to me but to those white people who put up the 'Whites Only' signs and who talk about 'The Coloured Problem'. I know that I'm not part of this and I turn the knob and find pop music.

The Union Stadium is where all the coloured schools in Joburg gather every year for one day in March to compete in the coloured schools inter-school athletics competition. Many of the boys and girls become one hundred metre and four hundred metre and high jump and long jump champions.

165

'I hear you're a good runner?' Uncle Tony says with a wink. He's chewing one of his Stimorols which I didn't even see him pop into his mouth.

'Who told you that?'

'Ah, I've got my contacts.'

I pause for a moment to take in the drab surroundings of minedumps, bluegum trees and rusty disused mines. This is where my friends and I sometimes come to hang out in the afternoons. But today there's nobody around and there's a sad breeze blowing.

'You know how the teachers divide you into groups for the athletics competitions – the Lions, Tigers, Cheetahs and Leopards…'

He nods.

'Well I was so slow, the teachers added another house just for me – the Tortoises.'

He chuckles. 'But you've got a fast mind.'

Uncle Tony may not be generous with his scrambled eggs and the odd tip, but he's dishing out one or two compliments today.

'You wanna hear my Afrikaner joke?'

He nods.

'This Afrikaner, his name is Poephol van der Merwe.'

'Poephol?'

'Ja,' I nod. 'That's his actual name and surname. So everywhere he goes people laugh at him. Poephol van der Merwe ha ha ha! Poephol van der Merwe ha ha ha! One day Poephol gets tired of being teased. He goes to the Births and Deaths offices. He tells the clerk behind the counter, "Hey look, I'd like to change my name." "And what is your name, sir?" "Poephol van der Merwe." "I see," the clerk says. "Well, it will cost you fifty rand to change it." "No problem," Poephol says. "And what would you like to change it to?" the clerk asks him. "To Poephol Pretorius."'

Uncle Tony gives a smile – which could've been a laugh muffled by a sudden gust of wind. He says, 'I hear you're thinking of joining the army?'

I give him a suspicious look and shake my head.

'What?' he says.

'You're hearing a lot of funny stuff these day. Change your contacts.'

He chuckles. 'So you're not thinking of joining the army?'

I shake my head. I pick up stones and fling them at a distant rusty tin. One hits the target and the hollow sound pleases me.

'Why not?'

'Because we should have one army, not a white one here, a coloured one there.'

'Where did you hear these things?' he asks, looking surprised.

'My contacts.'

He finds this funnier than my Afrikaner joke.

HALF AN HOUR later we're in Newclare. And suddenly Uncle Tony takes a wrong turn, down a street and towards the flats instead of the stadium.

'Uncle Tony…'

'Don't worry,' he says. 'I'm going to see a friend quickly. We've got lots of time.'

There's something about adults that amuses me a little. When you go somewhere with them they don't tell you the whole plan. You're on your way to Venus and then suddenly they turn left. You ask, 'What's happening?' and they say, 'I've got a friend on Pluto, I have to see him about something – it'll only take a minute.'

But I don't really mind, and even visiting a friend is a kind of entertainment. The main thing is I'm out of Riverlea and seeing new places and faces.

'Who's he?' I ask.

'People I work with.'

Aha! One friend has become 'people'. Singular has turned to plural. This means only one thing: his friend is a woman.

We make our way to the flats – rows and rows of rectangular blocks like gigantic dominoes, all three storeys high and named after girls in alphabetical order – there's 'ANNE', 'BEATRICE', 'CAROL', 'DINAH', 'EDITH'. The graffiti writers have spared none of these ladies who all have cryptic messages and rude words scrawled on them.

BOOM AND THEM
THE WARLORDS
WHEN DAYS ARE DARK FRENDS ARE FEW

My English teacher, Mrs Merckle, says, 'People are strange: ask them to write something on the blackboard or in a book and they're too shy to do it. But give them a wall and they'll really get going.'

Hilda Court is the one we want, and what a busy place! On its shady side teenage boys are smoking cigarettes and holding up the building with one foot flat against it.

On the ground floor a fat man in a vest leans over the iron railing and stares, with glazed eyes, at IRENE.

Directly above him, a woman in a pink nightgown, her hair in symmetrical rows of rollers, is trying to have a private conversation in public with another woman on the ground far away. Some words she shouts out loud, like 'me' and 'Blue Danube' (a nightclub) and 'tonight'. But the rest of the story is conveyed in a home-made sign language. And, most amusing to me, is the whisper across the courtyard of the name 'Horace' – the loudest whisper I have ever heard.

The girl in the courtyard still can't hear and Uncle Tony shouts, 'Horace!'

The woman in the rollers uses more sign language to show him what she thinks of him.

Uncle Tony and I laugh and he blows her a kiss.

Where are we going? I still don't know as we begin to mount the stairs. I quickly invent a game, called 'guess where we're going'. And my answer is half right half wrong: top storey is right, second door is not.

On the top floor, right where the stairs end, someone has spilt something and it awaits us like a welcome mat. Actually it's more a map than a mat, a continent of spilt Coke.

Uncle Tony avoids it but I deliberately step, with one shoe, into its interior – to test its stickiness. And, ja, it's sticky; my shoe takes a split second longer than usual to come away.

My game continues, from doors 211 to 216. I slow down just a little as we pass each door, to have a peep inside.

211 – A girl has a baby up on the kitchen sink and she's trying to feed it something that it keeps spitting out.

212 – Closed.

213 – I don't see anybody around but the radio is on and the Kinks are singing 'Lola'.

214 – A bare-chested man is sitting at a kitchen table scratching his armpit while reading a newspaper.

215 – The door is only partially open and all I can see is a kitchen sink.

And 216 is where we want to be. I would never have guessed.

Uncle Tony knocks and says 'Kor-kor' and opens the door. If the owner didn't want us inside, it's too late now.

'Slaap julle nog?' Uncle Tony calls out. (Are you all still sleeping?)

No answer – which, if you think about it, could very well mean 'Yes'.

The flat is small. From where I'm standing I can see parts of every room – kitchen, toilet, lounge and bedroom.

'Tony, is that you?' a woman's voice calls from the bedroom.

'Hey, Judy! You still in bed?'

'No no.' Judy rushes out of the bedroom. She's dressed, perfumed and clearly happy to see Tony. She greets me warmly. She's pretty, with laughing brown eyes beneath frizzy hair. She's wearing jeans and a striped beige and brown jersey.

She smiles at me and says, 'Are you Kuller?'

I nod. What has Uncle Tony been telling her about me?

They sit down at the kitchen table and I step over to the lounge window so that they can chat.

From the window I look down onto a busy road. Cars, mostly old and cranky, roll by. Across the road is a greengrocer called Bill's Farm, and women and kids are going inside and coming out with half pumpkins, cabbages, potatoes and tomatoes.

And what do I see parked nearby? The Fanny Farmers van! Fanny Farmers is a mobile confectionery shop that goes from township to township on Saturdays selling fresh bread, buns, biscuits and sweets. About three o'clock this afternoon Fanny Farmers will park for a while on the corner of Colorado Drive and Galana to sell its baked delights to the people of Riverlea. But here it is in Newclare.

I open the window and sniff the air. Fanny Farmers' delicious smell doesn't make it up to the top of Hilda Court.

In my trouser pocket are two twenty cent coins that I've been saving for today. According to my budget the money will be spent at the Union Stadium on a Coke, salt 'n vinegar Simba chips and a packet of humbugs.

Now, I reach into my pocket and, with my fingers, I have a last dance with the coins – because plans are being revised and we will be parting company sooner than expected.

My new budget list is: one Fanny Farmers Chelsea bun, one can of Fanta, one packet of humbugs.

I go down to Fanny Farmers and buy my Chelsea bun. It sticks to my hands immediately as if it always wanted to be with me. Next I go to a nearby corner café where I buy the Fanta and the humbugs. I put the humbugs in my pocket where the coins used to be.

Now, where is the best place to have my feast? There are two options and each has its risks.

Option one: I go back upstairs to flat 216 and offer Uncle Tony and his dressed up friend some. Grown-ups say 'no thanks' more often than we do, but I can't take the risk.

Option two: I sit here on the pavement and some of these Newclare boys come along and take my goodies and run. I've heard stories about Newclare tsotsis.

I decide to go for option two. I find a spot on the pavement in the warm winter sun and begin to eat my bun. What a treat! I've never even looked at one from so close let alone eaten one! It's almost as big as a whole cake. If Ma were here right now she'd cut this bun into five equal parts without flinching. Even if there is nobody to share it with, Ma divides things into five out of habit.

One day Ma had to divide a jam doughnut between me, Derek, Shaune and Alison. She broke it into three equal parts and gave a piece each to Derek, Shaune and Alison. 'What about me, Ma?' I asked sadly. 'You can have the hole,' Ma said.

That didn't really happen, it's just a joke I made up right now because I'm so happy.

I bite a piece of bun, keep it in my mouth and take a sip of Fanta. I let the two mix, slowly, slowly. And then I swallow.

If I were in Riverlea right now there would be a crowd of guys all shouting, 'Gee stuk, nix dols, nix mangas.' But here in Newclare it's just me and me alone.

We used to live in Newclare before we moved to Riverlea. But that was many years ago, before I was four years old. I don't know where it was, down this way towards the railway line or up there towards Western Coloured Township.

I remember the day Grace took me to a school to get vaccinated, carrying me on her back and making me believe that we were on our way to some big party. I believed it even up to the moment when the nurse came and dabbed my arm with spirits.

Whenever I get even the faintest whiff of spirits I think about that day, and I think about Grace.

I remember coming home from my granny's with Auntie Jenny carrying me some of the way and making me walk when she got out of breath. Down Hamilton Street, past the hospital, the Ebenezer Church, across the traffic circle, the bicycle shop, the butchery.

'Walk a little bit,' my aunt urged me. 'We're almost there. Your mummy's waiting for her big boy.'

But when we reached our home, the doors were locked and nobody was home. Where were my parents? Gone to the shops to return minutes later? Or to the movies to return an hour or two later? In those days an hour lasted a whole day!

There was nothing we could do but wait. Auntie Jenny sat flat on the stoep with her legs stretched out in front of her. When I became restless my aunt tried to keep me amused by singing:

Bobbejaan klim die berg
So haastig en so lustig
Bobbejaan klim die berg
So haastig en so lustig
Bobbejaan klim die berg
Om die boere te vererg
Hoera virrie jollie bobbejaan

It was a song about a baboon scampering up a mountain to flee from angry farmers.

Now what is it that turned my mind to that day? Maybe it's Fanny Farmers that made me think of farmers and the baboon in the song. Or it's because I'm in Newclare where I first heard the song. Or because I'm going to spend the day with Auntie Jenny's boyfriend.

I also wonder how it's going with Conos at the doctor where he's being weighed and measured.

If Conos were here I would give him half my bun any time. We share everything right down the middle. I remember in primary school when we'd sometimes end up with three sweets between us – and we'd share it: one for you, one for me, and one of us would bite the third one in half.

Now we're bigger and we do it differently: one of us would say, 'It's OK, you take it, next time I'll take it.'

But Vino, our other best friend, he's different. That guy is so stingy, we joke that he could peel an orange from his pocket and slip it into his mouth, piece by piece, without anyone even noticing.

A couple of weeks ago, Vino and I were walking home from school as we do most afternoons. He asked if it was OK if he popped in at the shops and I said sure.

He bought a big packet of viennas and chips. He turned to me and said their housekeeper Promise asked him to buy it for her before he left for school this morning.

That was the biggest salt 'n vinegar lie I've heard in my life. Like Promise has got spare cash on a Thursday afternoon when

172

the whole of Riverlea is going to sit down to a lunch of bread and jam!

THE CAPE COLOURED Corps does not disappoint.

Before the event some of the soldiers who got drunk at our house on Saturday, spot Uncle Tony and me in the stands. They come up to chat and to give us a few friendly punches.

Corporal January shakes my hand and he feels the stickiness. 'Whatsit?' he asks me.

'Just a Chelsea bun I had for breakfast.' I tell him I'm sorry.

'It's OK,' he says. 'If I get hungry later on I can sommer lick my hand.'

These are the stars of today's show and they're chatting and joking with me and Uncle Tony! And all over the terraces eyes are fixed on us!

Then a commander blows a whistle and the show begins.

The soldiers are dressed in different coloured vests. Some in orange, some in white and some in blue.

They line up in no particular order and start doing physical exercises, kicking out their legs, clapping their hands, touching the green grass with their fingertips. Then there's a rhythmic swopping of places and a thunderous final clap and – they've formed the South African flag.

The grandstands burst into loud applause.

There's more to come.

The soldiers lie down on their backs and form a huge circle that is outer orange, middle white and inner blue, like a giant target.

Then a military helicopter appears from nowhere with a loud clack-clack-clack and hovers in the air above the target. A soldier appears in the door of the copter...

We hold our breath.

He jumps. His parachute opens. He floats comfortably down and lands in the centre of the target.

We stand up and cheer.

The show ends at about five in the afternoon and it starts getting chilly—with a wind that could easily have blown our parachutist off target. But we're in luck. Uncle Tony spots a friend who has a bakkie. He tells us to get onto the back—where I suck on my last humbug.

It's been a perfect afternoon.

Home secrets

It's Wednesday afternoon and I'm sitting at the kitchen table. It's only five o'clock but already the sun is going down, because it's winter. Agnes left an hour and a half ago and now Ma is moving between the kitchen sink and the coal stove, cooking tomato bredie.

I'm illustrating my school poetry anthology. Every week Mr Brown gives us a roneoed poem or he tells us to write the poem down ourselves. The poems go on the right and the illustrations on the left.

This poem is by G.K. Chesterton and it's called 'The Donkey'. I tell Ma what it's all about:

'You know how people are always saying the donkey's a stupid animal and all that?'

Ma says, 'Mhm.'

'Now, in this poem, this donkey has had enough of being called stupid and he reminds us that once upon a time, in the days of the Bible, Jesus Christ once rode on his back!'

Alison comes into the kitchen and asks Ma if she brought her a sweet. Ma calls out to Shaune having a bath to go easy on the hot water. She's peeling potatoes, and I'm about to give up explaining the poem when she says:

'Ai die donkey is 'n wonderlike ding.'

I laugh, and then the front door opens. Dad comes in, and I stop laughing. The five or six things that happen next happen every night.

He comes into the kitchen and gives Ma a peck on the cheek. Alison runs from the room and into his arms. He rubs his bristly beard against her neck and makes her scream. He takes a peek into the pots and Ma slaps his wrist with a dishcloth. The kitchen is warm and the tomato bredie smells deliciously spicy. But now it has to compete with the aroma of wood and cigarette smoke.

He has a bath, has supper, swears at me – or Derek or Shaune but mostly at me – for something I didn't do, or did do or am doing too slowly.

He works in a factory in the bottom end of town making furniture. Sometimes there's 'a big order' that has to be completed on a certain date and he works overtime. Then he comes home late and he can hardly eat or talk (because he's too tired) or swear (because I'm fast asleep in bed). Ma looks at him and says, 'Shame!' I lie in bed and say, in my mind, 'Good!'

Tonight he changes the ritual slightly. He wants to talk to Ma and it's private – I know because he gives me that, 'I wish you could disappear' look.

I get up and go to the lounge with my anthology and I listen to him from there. He knows I could be eavesdropping so he goes into the code that he and Ma use.

He says, 'Dipirripid yoporripou gporropo?'

Ma says, 'Yeperripes.'

They exchange a few more sentences and then Uncle Tony comes in from work and they stop. And the next thing, Ma's handing out instructions in ordinary English:

'Shaune, when are you getting into the bath?'

'Christopher, how many times do I have to tell you to put that radio softer!'

I once replied, 'Can you speak up, Ma. Can't hear you, the radio's too loud.'

She didn't think it was funny.

At about seven o'clock the food is dished up – seven plates on the kitchen table – and Ma calls us to get it and find a place to sit.

We kids take our plates to the lounge. The three adults sit at the kitchen table. Our latest dog Brucie sits by the kitchen door waiting for the scraps.

So far Dad hasn't sworn at anyone. But the night is young.

After supper, the adults are still sitting at the kitchen table talking about their jobs – mostly about nasty white bosses which all three seem to have in common.

Then little Alison interrupts the conversation with a tap of Uncle Tony's knee. She has something to show him.

'Lookit Chris's nice book,' she says, and hands him my diary! I'm there at the sink washing dishes watching this and my heart skips a beat or two.

My diary! How did she get hold of it? This is what happens when there are too many people in one house: even your secret place is not a secret place any more.

Where was it hidden you might be wondering? Let me tell you by paraphrasing a popular Afrikaans poem:

In Riverlea was a street
In the street was a house
In the house was a room
In the room was a cupboard
In the cupboard were five drawers
The top drawer was for Chris's shirts
The second was for Derek's shirts
The third drawer was for Shaune's shirts
The fourth drawer was for all our socks
Pull the fourth drawer out altogether
Underneath this drawer is a secret space
In this space is a diary
In this diary are Chris's secrets

But now that diary is in Uncle Tony's hands. He says, 'Thank you. Nice.'

Dad is explaining something to him about measuring planks. 'Pienaar tells me to cut them six by three…'

177

Ma interrupts, 'Pienaar or Visser?'

'What?' Dad says, 'Visser, I said Visser.'

'You said Pienaar.'

Dad says, 'It doesn't matter.' A hint of irritation has crept into his voice.

Ma can do three, four or five things at once, but Dad is a one-thing-at-a-time man, and right now there are too many things happening in the kitchen.

The stove has lost so much heat that you can put your hand on its plates without getting burnt. But it's getting hot in the kitchen.

'Look, look,' Alison insists.

I dry my hands.

'Just now, angel,' Uncle Tony says.

Dad is still trying to tell his story and Uncle Tony puts the diary down in front of him.

My hands are dried now and I reach out for my diary. But Uncle Tony has a thumb on it. I'm not allowed to disturb them but I want my diary before he decides to open it. Its contents could bring this whole house down! I take a bold step towards my book of secrets.

'Christopher.' It's Ma, and I realise that she had called my name before but I hadn't heard.

There are three kinds of 'Christopher' that Ma calls: a normal 'Christopher', a 'Chris-ter-fer' with the syllables spaced out, and a loud, sharp 'CHRISTOPHER'. I hear the second one and look at her.

'Fetch my cigarettes.'

I don't want to go; I want to stay here and make sure my diary doesn't get opened. But they're all talking, and if I go quickly I could be back in seconds. I race down the passage and into my parents' room. The packet of cigarettes is on the dressing table and the little box of matches is on top of it. I grab them, and seconds later I'm back.

They're still talking and Uncle Tony's thumb is still on my diary. Nothing has changed. I go to Uncle Tony's side. But now

Dad has begun to take his eyes off Uncle Tony to glare at me. I'm beginning to irritate him. But he needn't worry, all I want is my diary.

'Ashtray,' Ma says.

'Ma?'

'Bring me an ashtray; where do you think I'm going to put the ash.' And she lets out one of those sighs.

Ashtray, ashtray, where's the nearest ashtray! Lounge. I find one on a doily. It's got four parking spaces, one for each of the three smokers plus an extra one for me – just in case I suddenly light up one of Ma's Van Rijns because, to tell the truth, I'm stressing.

Stressing that my book of secrets might be opened up at any second now. I don't want them to see the entry about Conos and why he couldn't come with me to see the soldiers at the Union Stadium.

But most of all, I don't want them to see the stuff about the three of them. Ma might laugh, Uncle Tony might be embarrassed. But Dad? I don't think he'll like what I've written about him. For example:

<u>*Saturday 27 April*</u>
I wish Ma and Dad would stop speaking in that code of theirs. I've cracked it and mastered it and actually I can speak it better than them. Earlier this evening Ma said something to Dad in that language. He didn't understand what she was saying and I very nearly told him.

When I bring the ashtray, I see that Uncle Tony is busy flipping through my diary. He's concentrating more on what Dad is saying, but he only has to spot his name as he flips through to stop and read.

'Uncle Tony, may I have my diary?' My hand is already on it, yanking it from him.

'What the hell?' Dad says. 'What do you think you're doing?'

'Chris,' Ma says. 'Can't you just ask nicely?'

'It's my diary.'

'But can't you see Uncle Tony is reading…'

'But it's…it's private.'

'Private!' Dad says. 'What do you mean, what secrets do you have?'

My dad's head is so close to me now that one or two flecks of spit land on my face.

This is exactly how I knew he would react. I read once that in Sweden children have rights. That if you as much as opened a child's letter in that country you could go to jail. But here in this country children have no rights. A teacher can beat you silly and all your parents will say is, 'You deserved it.'

I look to Ma for help, but she's not interested, hiding behind a smoke cloud and pretending that she can't see me.

I think Ma and Dad have a pact: if you scold the kids I won't interfere and vice versa. It was so nice before Dad came home, when Ma and I were doing the poem and talking about the donkey. But now Ma is a different person.

At school Mr Fasser calls Evan Adams a santjiebol (a bad word for an albino) just because Evan is very fair and has lots of freckles. I don't think a teacher should be saying such things to a child. But most kids laugh when Fasser says that. And those that don't laugh don't do anything about it anyway. I wonder if white kids here in South Africa have rights and stuff like that. I would like to ask them but I don't know any. And according to apartheid I shouldn't be talking to white kids anyway.

I think all this rights business has something to do with apartheid.

Oh God help me! Uncle Tony has found an entry. My face gets unbearably hot. What has he found?

He reads out loud:

Ma keeps shouting at us—me, Derek and Shaune—for sticking old chewing gum underneath the tables and chairs and in the vase. But you don't have to be a rocket scientist to know who the culprit is: Uncle Tony the Stimorol man!

'What a nerve!' Dad says. 'Apologise now, you little…!'

'Sorry, Kuller.' Alison says, looking up at me with big sad eyes. She has been here all the time, forgotten in the excitement. Her voice is so sweet and gentle – and afraid – that she sounds like somebody else.

'But Nick,' Uncle Tony says, 'he's right! It's one of those bad habits I should've left in Cape Town.' He turns to Ma. 'I'm not buying gum any more. Sorry, Shirl.'

I grab my diary before more secrets come spilling out of it. But Dad sees it as an act of defiance. He glares at me.

All that happened on 19 June. But there is no record in my diary of it – or anything else since.

The Stimorol man hits
the road

Uncle Tony packed his bags and left.

His orange underpants and his other loud clothes disappeared from the line. His little brown travelling bag with its tiny brush and comb and mirror. His toothpaste and brush, gone.

The smell of his Brylcreem followed about three or four days later.

No more boarder. No more scrambled eggs on a Saturday morning.

It wasn't my diary entry that caused his departure. He departed on good terms – but stayed on in Joburg.

He never got married to Auntie Jenny, but left her with a baby boy that my aunt named William. Uncle Tony wasn't around to help choose a name.

Sometimes Ma would come from work and say, 'I saw Uncle Tony today. He sends his regards.'

Dad too, after visiting a friend would say to Ma, 'Guess who I saw today?'

Agnes didn't even have to be told he was gone. No case on the wardrobe, no Brylcreem in the bathroom. And, most of all, no tackies under the bed!

I don't know how her wages were readjusted – that was a matter between Agnes and Ma. All I know is that she was happy.

'Now you have fewer eggs to lay and chickens to hatch.'

'Oh yes!'

AFTER HE LEFT my aunt I didn't really miss Uncle Tony. There were other things that began to preoccupy my mind: girls, for one; learning to smoke cigarettes; taking my first drink – all the ordinary things that teenagers my age were up to.

But also the odd things that no other teenagers seemed to be doing: devouring books, writing my first real poems and stories, turning my attention with less confusion and more anger to the apartheid government.

Sometimes, though, I did think of Uncle Tony. At least every once in a while. Something triggered it – maybe when I saw a pack of Stimorol gum advertised on TV, or I smelt Brylcreem. Or it was something so tenuous or transient that I couldn't put my finger on it.

I thought mostly of that step-by-step trip to the Union Stadium. How we talked about things, about life, the army.

And suddenly it hit me that my father had never willingly taken me somewhere with him – to a movie, to a sports event, to watch the rag parade in town.

It's true that as coloureds – or 'non-whites' as the government liked calling us – there were not many interesting places we could go to. But it was not the places I would have wanted to visit, it was the journey there.

Maybe, who knows, my dad might have stopped calling me by those four-letter aliases that he spat at me so often. He might have seen that there was actually something worthwhile brewing in that seemingly absent-minded head of mine.

LET'S PLAY WITH this idea a little.

Let's say I'm going to pop in at Conos's. I knock on the door, his ma opens.

'Hi, Auntie Daphne, is Conos in?'

She gives me a puzzled look and says, 'It's Thursday today, Chris.'

Thursday? Then I remember! Every Thursday Conos and his dad take in a movie. Tomorrow morning when I see him at school, he'll have a grown-up air about him.

'Of course, Auntie Daphne! I don't know what I was thinking.'

Well, I am in the area – Vino lives four or five doors away from Conos. Let me go see what he's up to. I'm about to knock when I peep through the window. Vino and his dad are sitting at the dining room table. Vino's schoolbooks are spread all over and father and son are on the verge of solving an algebra problem together.

It's such a special moment: father and son together, discovering Maths.

Rather than disturb them, I turn on my heel and head for home, where I find *my* dad in his vest and shorts, blowing smoke towards the ceiling, listening to George and Rita on the radio.

'Where do you come from?' he says. 'Your mother's been…'

'Never mind that now, Dad,' I say, pulling up a chair near the couch where he's lying down.

'What?'

'Listen, Dad. I've just been to Conos and Vino's and they're both with their dads and they're bonding…'

'What?'

'Bonding, Dad.'

While we're looking at each other there's a sudden burst of canned laughter from the radio.

'Listen here,' he says, sitting up straight so that I don't miss a word, 'if you really wanna do some bonding then go watch that new James Bond film this weekend. Now go see what your mother wants.'

Thanks, Dr No, for shaking me out of that dream.

ABOUT SIX YEARS later, I literally did bump into Uncle Tony myself. I was coming out of one of the local shops, and knocked into this guy. The first thing I saw were the tackies, the loud shirt, the familiar pockmarked face and the Brylcreemed hair – shorter now as the afro had gone out of fashion.

'Kuller!' he cried, genuinely happy to see me.

'Uncle Tony! Howzit?'

But I could see that things were not going so well with him. He had dark spots in his face. His clothes were creased. His tackies needed a good scrub. His fingernails were long and packed with grime or printer's ink.

'Hah, a moustache,' he teased me, pointing at the dark stripe on my upper lip. And then he asked me if I had a girlfriend yet.

I was happy to see our one-time boarder, but then he said something that changed my opinion of him forever.

'How is er whatsisname…William?' he asked me.

'You mean your *son* William?' I asked him, shocked.

'Yes, him,' he nodded.

I was speechless for a while, even a little embarrassed. This, I felt, was more serious than merely spitting gum into a vase.

'Don't you think I should be asking *you* that question?'

'Hey, Kuller!' He tried to put an ink-stained hand on my shoulder but I stepped back. 'You still so serious about everything.' He asked me for a few rands for a beer but I ignored him and said goodbye for good.

Street secrets

A section of the street from lamp-post to lamp-post is our football field. One of those goalposts is outside the Jacksons' gate, which remains open all day. From the street you can see all the way into the backyard where their dog Dinky, tied to a metre-long chain, barks non-stop and runs a semicircle into the ground.

Dinky can see us – or more importantly, his three masters Chubby, Vince and Gavin. When one of them comes into sight Dinky goes wild and barks his head off. Later in the afternoon, around five thirty, the family car rolls into the yard. Dinky's vision is obscured and he shuts up for the day. Poor Dinky, watching one section of a street soccer game every day seems to be his only entertainment.

The Jackson boys' father is Uncle Gordon and their ma is Auntie Sheila – factory workers both, furniture and dressmaking like almost everybody else's dad and ma.

Uncle Gordon drives an old but reliable bluish grey 1959 Zephyr. He bought it early this year, from his boss or his boss's wife or some other white person. People say if you buy a car second-hand you're buying another man's problems. But nobody in Riverlea can afford a brand new car. And in any case, if you ever do drive one you'll have the jealous white traffic cops stopping you on every corner asking you: 'Which white man did you steal this from?'

The Zephyr is not in bad condition. Every morning it takes Uncle Gordon and Auntie Sheila to work. And every evening it brings them home. Every morning one of the boys washes the car, from top to tyres, with soap and water.

On Saturdays the Zephyr stands still. That's when Uncle Gordon relaxes in his lounge drinking brandy and Coke and listening to Fausto Papetti dance records. He invariably has two friends visiting him, not always the same two friends, but there are always two – no more, no less. It's like the rule at Coronation hospital's ICU ward: 'No more than two visitors per patient.'

On Sunday afternoons Uncle Gordon goes down to the football field like the rest of Riverlea to watch a football game. The whole world around him is chanting and screaming and dancing and laughing. But not Uncle Gordon. He stands on one spot throughout the match, quiet, expressionless in his dark grey safari suit and his grey socks that come up to his calves and fold over. Uncle Gordon is always clean-shaven, hair oiled and combed into shiny waves.

But more mysterious than Uncle Gordon is the Jacksons' widowed grandmother, Ouma Marta (Uncle Gordon's mother) who lives with them. She sits in the house all day. We never ever see her face but we hear her voice all the time, calling one of her grandsons:

'Chubby, come and chop the wood!'

'Vincent, come and clean up where you messed!'

'Gavin, you have to go to the shop!'

We're of course playing soccer in the street, a mere ten metres from the bedroom window from where she shouts for the boys.

We want to know what Ouma Marta looks like. Is she fat or thin? Big or small? Grey or almost grey? Does she take snuff, drink alcohol? And why does she never come out and show her face to the world?

All the oumas move around, no matter how old they are, how hard of hearing, how painful the arthritis or whether they've forgotten their teeth at home or think they've forgotten them at home.

But Ouma Marta is a mystery, a voice behind a curtain.

We ask her grandsons:

'Why don't we ever see your ouma?'

Chubby, the youngest and wittiest of the three, says: 'Why do yous want to see her? Does she owe yous money?'

Vince says: 'You guys want to start trouble, I can see that.'

Gavin doesn't even answer, he just spits on the ground and says, 'Are we playing ball today or what?'

One afternoon when the three brothers are not around, we decide to lure her outside. It's Crowbar's idea. He leaves us leaning against the hedging outside and he says: 'Watch.'

He goes up to the door.

'Ouma Marta!' he calls out to her. 'Ouma Marta!'

'Yes!' her voice comes from somewhere inside the house.

'Come outside quick!'

'What for?'

'There's a white man outside here who wants to talk to you.'

'About what?'

'He didn't say, Ouma. I think he wants you to sign something.'

'Sign what?'

'I don't know, Ouma, he didn't tell me.'

Silence.

'Ouma?'

Still silence.

Finally we give up and go back to our game.

Then one day one of us does set eyes on Ouma Marta. This privilege falls to none other than my brother Derek. It happens one afternoon when Derek wanders into the Jackson yard in search of our ball. Neither Chubby nor Vince nor Gavin are at home. But we want to play a soccer match and this is the yard where the ball slept after yesterday's game and we want it now.

Derek proceeds to look for the ball: coalbox – not there; in an old car tyre – nothing doing; under a pile of planks – no luck.

Suddenly Derek needs to pee. But the Jackson toilet, only a mere two metres away, is definitely out of bounds. Ouma Marta would never let him come inside. But this is not a problem at all because boys pee anywhere – in the street, against a wall, in the veld, behind a hedge – as long as girls aren't around.

So Derek has a pee right there in the yard. And while he's making a nice big figure-of-eight in the dust, Dinky starts barking.

'Shut up, Dinky,' Derek hisses, because if the dog doesn't keep quiet Ouma Marta might peep from behind the curtains and see him fouling up their yard.

But Dinky just barks louder. So Derek pees on Dinky, a good squirt right in his cheeky little face.

Dinky is so shocked that he dives into his kennel and proceeds to shake the pee off himself. Derek has a hearty chuckle and can't wait to get back to the street to tell us this story. But, suddenly he hears a familiar voice demanding to know:

'What the hell d'you think you're doing?'

Derek quickly parks his little Zephyr. He looks up. It's Ouma Marta standing in the doorway, in person!

She's fat and seems to be having a big problem standing up. 'What the hell d'you think...' seems to have taken all her strength and she's having a tough time getting her breath back. One can see why oumas don't play ball in the street, even though she has the right language for street ball. Only yesterday Gavin passed the ball to the opposition by mistake and Derek said to him, 'What the hell d'you think you're doing?' But you have to say it a hundred times in one match without getting tired – plus you have to score a couple of goals.

Derek looks at her and he is stunned. She has something he has never seen on an ouma before.

Ouma Marta realises what he's looking at and disappears into the house and slams the door shut.

My brother does eventually find the ball. He brings it to us and we play our game. But that afternoon he is not quite the Derek who tackles, dribbles and scores.

That night, when we're alone, he says, 'I got a secret.'

'What?' I ask.

'I can't tell you.' And with a sigh, he lays his head on the pillow and stares at the ceiling.

I know he'll tell me eventually. But first I have to jump through a couple of hoops.

'I always tell you things,' I remind him.

'Like what?'

Damnit! I was hoping he wouldn't ask me that. 'Like…'

'Ah, you see!'

'Well, maybe you don't even *have* a secret!'

'I got a secret,' he assures me.

I won't tell anybody,' I promise. 'God can strike me stone dead if I do.'

He shakes his head and I decide to try a different tack.

'OK, maybe you'll tell me tomorrow morning,' I say and I switch off the light.

After a moment's silence he blurts it out – in the dark. It is unbelievable, made more unbelievable by the darkness. I switch the light back on and dare him to say it again.

'Ouma Marta has got a beard.'

'Where did you see it?'

'On her chin.'

It's a good joke, but the wrong time. Shaune and Alison are snoring away, Ma and Dad are trying to fall asleep in the room next door, and now we've got the giggles.

'On her chinny-chin-chin,' he says and we laugh as if it's Saturday afternoon at the movies and we're watching *The Three Stooges*.

THE NEXT DAY, the first person I tell is Agnes, but she doesn't seem at all surprised.

'D'you know what's a beard, Agnes?'

'Yes,' she says, stroking her chin. 'Many people in Soweto have them.'

'I'm talking about a woman, Agnes, a gogo.'

'Yes, men and women have them.'

Agnes is so disinterested that I don't feel like I've broken a pledge. I go in search of Conos.

'Hey, what you telling me now!' Conos says.

Now I feel like I've broken a pledge.

'Just don't tell anybody.'

'Ten Bibles on my head,' he says.

A few hours later he tells Crowbar, but to show he can still be trusted with secrets he only uses initials, like this:

'There's three brothers whose initials are C and G and V. Their father has a car whose initial is Z.'

Crowbar nods and goes, 'Ja, ja, ja,' after each initial.

'Their ouma's got a beard.'

Crowbar tells Rathead who carries the story to Derek, who has already told two or three guys anyway. This beard story is spreading so fast, we don't know who told who any more.

Then, the inevitable happens. One afternoon we're playing our usual football in the street and all three Jackson brothers are in the game. Rathead's got the ball and he's getting ready to score. Chubby attempts to slide-tackle Rathead, misses the ball, but gets Rathead on the ankle – eina! We don't have a referee so the fouls are sorted out with a 'Voetsek!' or a punch.

'You playing dirty, sonny!' Rathead snarls.

'This is a man's game, my laaitie,' Chubby says. 'Why don't you go play doll-house with your sister!'

Rathead says, 'Why don't *you* go play with your oupa!'

In the street game of gwarra there is only one rule: no teasing a man's ma or any member of the family that is dead. Anyone else is fair game.

'My oupa's dead, sonny!' Chubby half sobs, looking around for a brick to bash in Rathead's head.

'Your oupa's dead? Then who's that behind the curtains with a beard?'

ONE AFTERNOON THE Zephyr is in the driveway. It's not supposed to be there because it should have taken Uncle Gordon and Auntie Sheila to work.

It's easy to ignore a car in the driveway, but not the Zephyr because it's causing Dinky to bark all the time: it's obstructing Dinky's view and he can't watch his three masters play ball. He can hear the commotion in the street but he can't see what the hell's going on. This makes him mad and he barks non-stop.

Ouma Marta yells from the bedroom window: 'Sê daai hond hy moet sy bek hou!' (Tell that dog to shut up!)

But nobody can get him to stay quiet.

'Maybe if I go pee on him,' Derek whispers to me.

We all know the problem is the Zephyr.

'Why didn't your dad take the car to work?' Crowbar asks Gavin.

'The brakes,' he says. 'There's something wrong with the brakes.'

The next day the car is still there – and the next, and the next. To stop Dinky from going crazy we move our game to the football field. It's just down the road but it's not as nice as our old spot – lots of boys come asking for a game and you can't refuse them and before you know it you're playing twenty a side. If you get a chance to kick the ball once, you're lucky.

On Sunday there's no sign of Uncle Gordon in his lounge, with his two friends, listening to Fausto Papetti dance music.

'Can you keep a secret?' Derek asks me.

'Ja, of course.'

'You couldn't keep the last one.'

'I only told Conos and I told him to tell no one.'

'Uncle Gordon is in jail.'

'What for? How? Who told you?'

'Chubby. That's all he told me.'

This news spreads to all the boys as fast as the beard story did. But we never find out why Uncle Gordon is in prison. He will be away for about a year.

In the meantime, the Jacksons make some adjustments. Vincent manages to drive the car deep into the backyard so that Dinky can shut up and watch the football match every afternoon. When it's time for gwarra the bearded Ouma Marta is top of the agenda:

'Tell your ouma there's a half price on blades at the OK.'

'Does she have hair on her chest too?'

But Uncle Gordon in jail? None of us ever utters a word about that, even though we all know. It's as if we're all keeping a secret.

Backyard blues

Our backyard is tiny. To walk across it from one outer fence to the other would take you less than a minute. But a lot can happen in that time and a lot happens in our backyard.

There's a wooden coalbox underneath the bedroom window. Every Monday morning Mr MacPhail delivers two sacks of coal. His lorry stops in the street outside. On the back is painted the slogan: 'Mac Won't Phail You'.

As far as Agnes and the other housekeepers are concerned though, it reads: 'Mac won't fail to coat all the washing on the line in a thick layer of black dust.' The women dart into the yards – it's a race against time – and pluck the sheets and shirts and stuff from the line.

Mac's men are black, made even blacker by their job. The bags, half the size of an adult, woven with a tough black cotton, are lumpy and heavy. The men carry the bags on their backs. One of them makes his way into our backyard. Our dog and another from a neighbour, their front legs bent low and teeth bared in a piercing snarl, make for his heels. But something about his matt black featurelessness stops them. They cry and scatter.

The man lumbers up to the coalbox. He does a low curtsy at the box and the coal comes tumbling out from the bag on his back, spilling with a rattling noise into the coalbox.

I am always fascinated as for a moment the man disappears into a black cloud. It subsides and there he is again. He straightens himself, turns around and ambles out of the yard, taking his empty sack with him.

He never says hullo or goodbye to me. Maybe because he doesn't speak a word of English. Maybe also because he can't find a better job; maybe because he's dirty all the time and there's coaldust in his throat and in his eyes and so, why bother to say anything to anyone?

THEN THERE'S THE dustman.

Every day the dustbin grows heavier as we pile into it ash from the stoves, potato, squash and pumpkin peels, cabbage husks, empty Koo baked beans and peas, mixed vegetables, Glenryck pilchards and Nestlé condensed milk cans, newspaper, hardened blobs of chewing gum, shoes with holes in their soles, a diary with most of the pages torn out, a dead rat, shrivelled up green peaches, an orange scrub rag that was once somebody's underpants – stuff like that.

And on Thursdays the dustmen come rolling in like a travelling circus. They are livelier than the coal men and you can hear them coming in their lorry, three, four, five streets away. Their noise is a loud combination of sharp whistling, phrases shouted out in Zulu, Tswana or Sotho, and the excited barking of dogs from Columbia Street, where they've been, to Ganges Street, where they will get to later.

'Amagoduka!' Agnes screams and runs to once again rescue her washing.

The dustmen are piles of rags in the shape of men in tackies without laces, pants without belts and shirts without buttons. They also have hankies, their four corners knotted, stuck on their heads, rags tied around their necks like scarves, around their waists and ankles.

When they run they flutter and the dogs go wild.

One of them comes running into our yard, shouting his war cry, an empty bin on one shoulder. A dog comes snapping at his tattered tackies. He shouts something at the dog in Zulu. It must surely mean something like: 'These tackies have killed better breeds than you.'

Either the dog understands Zulu or he gets a whiff of dog blood on the tackies because he catches brakes and makes a quick U-turn.

Agnes is in the backyard to rescue her washing from the cloud of dust the man is about to make. He spots her, and his eyes twinkle in his dusty face. He tells her she's lovely and that he has been in love with her for a long long time, throughout all these many Thursdays of dust and peels and ash. He sees dozens of women every day, but she is the one who makes him lose sleep the most.

She scowls and clicks her tongue and warns him not to mess up her clean washing.

Superlaaitie

Ma says I'm absent-minded.

I don't think I can argue with her; she has proved it over and over again. Like, for instance, she calls me to send me to the shop. She tells me to buy:

'A loaf of bread. A small tin of apricot jam. And twenty Rothmans.'

She gives me a one rand note and says, 'What must you buy?'

'Bread, apricot jam, Rothmans.'

'There you go,' Ma says, and there I go. I walk down the street. The Wills sisters are playing rhubarb, with their dresses shoved into their panties. I'm thinking of my radio serial and I hear one of them say:

'You think you funny?'

I look up. I don't believe what I've done: I've walked right into their den and Gloria, who was 'in' and notching up a very good score, was forced to step out of my way.

The other girls click their tongues.

'Sorry, I didn't mean it,' I tell them, but they don't believe me. I wouldn't deliberately bomb up their game unless I was with Marlon and Conos and them.

I go back to thinking about my serial, *The Man They Couldn't Kill*, on Springbok Radio, quarter past seven, after Paddy O'Byrne has read the news. In last night's episode David (the man they couldn't kill) got a message to go to a certain tree at about midnight. He gets there, looks up into the starry night sky and exclaims: 'Good heavens above!' And that's where the episode ended! Now I'm walking and wondering, what did he see? What was it that made him shout out, 'Good heavens above!'? A spaceship, maybe, with winged aliens disembarking and flying towards him. Or maybe it was some famous warrior from the past, aiming a weapon at him that could turn him into gas…

Next thing I'm thinking about a book that I'm busy reading. This boy, Joe, is at a boarding school and he's convinced that a ghost visits their dormitory in the middle of the night. Then one night he sees the ghost again. It disappears behind a cupboard. Joe gets up, torch in hand, and follows the spook, a smoky apparition, as it floats through a trapdoor and down a secret passage…It seems to be leading him somewhere – but where to? To what?

The next minute I realise I'm at the shop and Mr Petersen is shouting, 'Next!'

It's unbelievable. I walked down Flinders Street, crossed the football field, passed the Evangelical Bible Church, the community hall, the library and the rent office, walked right into Mr Petersen's shop. And I can't remember a thing of the journey. And here's Mr Petersen shouting 'Next!' in my ear!

'A loaf of bread, twenty Rothmans and…'

He nods at me a few times as if that's going to coax item number three out of my head.

'Condensed milk.'

I walk home with my three items, but the condensed milk is bothering me. I have a feeling it's the wrong item. When I get back home I test out my theory with Ma by putting all three items down on the kitchen table and looking at her. Immediately she picks up the tin of condensed milk and asks:

'What's this?'

'Aw, condensed milk – what you asked me to buy.'

She shakes her head.

'You said bread, cigarettes and condensed milk.'

'I did *not*!'

'OK, what did you say?'

'I said apricot jam. Ape. Ree. Kot. Jam!'

'Oh ja!' Now I remember.

Ma rolls her eyes upwards.

'I'll take it back.'

Of course you'll take it back.'

'And this?' I point to the bread and cigarettes. 'Is Ma sure Ma's happy with this stuff?' But Ma's not in the mood for sarcastic jokes now.

So I slide off the chair and retrace my steps. It's humiliating to go back to the shops with an item. The Wills girls are still playing rhubarb when I pass them. They spot the tin in my hands and begin to snigger. Samantha says, as I pass her:

'Pay attention next time!'

I once looked up in the dictionary the meaning of the word 'condense'. It means 'compress' and that means to make smaller or to reduce in size. But, I tell you, this tin is so big that everybody sees it in my hands, all the way to the shop and they all know why I'm taking it back. I hide it under my shirt but eventually I have to take it out and hand it back to Mr Petersen.

'My ma changed her mind; she wants apricot jam instead.'

Mr Petersen is so busy with customers he doesn't catch my joke. He swops the condensed milk for apricot jam and shouts:

'Next!'

MY MA JUST calls me absent-minded whenever my mind goes on one of its trips. But my dad gets seriously cross. Once he even hit me with his belt. I was about eight years old.

It's a Sunday morning and I'm about to polish my black shoes for church. I've got the black Nugget polish tin open, and I've got the brushes (one for polishing and one for shining) and of course the shoes.

I'm about to start the job when I spot one of my *Superman* comics on a lounge chair. I start flipping through it...and then I'm reading the story. And afterwards I'm sitting there on the stoep and imagining what it would be like if I were...Superlaaitie!

I'm sitting in the classroom and of course nobody knows my true identity – classmates, teachers, mother, father, sister, brothers, nobody. I have superpower X-ray vision, strength, speed, the works. We're doing an oral exam and I did not prepare for it yesterday. I was about to, but I saw, with my super-vision that an Arabian princess – Princess Fathima – had been abducted. The princess is pretty with long black hair and big brown eyes. And she's about my age.

My X-ray vision is so powerful that from our lounge in Flinders Street, Riverlea, Johannesburg, South Africa, I can see the kidnapping taking place all the way in Saudi Arabia.

Three men in Mecca Maintenance overalls enter the palace. But my suspicions are raised when I notice a spelling error on their backs: 'Mekca'. It's great to be Superlaaitie, but it's even better if Superlaaitie is a good speller. I train my Superlaaitie vision on the faces of the abductors to see if one of them is not my friend Marlon – but he's not among them. Marlon may be a bad speller, but he's no kidnapper.

I have to study for tomorrow's test, but there's a young girl who needs help right now. A young girl who needs the services of ... SUPERLAAITIE.

In New York Clark Kent always rushes into a telephone booth to change into Superman. Here in Riverlea there's a phone booth up there by the rent office. But it's not an appropriate changeroom for Superlaaitie – kids are always playing around in there trying to make a call without paying, and it smells like pee. I'm Superlaaitie and there's no way I'm travelling long-distance smelling like pee.

So I do my changing on top of the minedumps where nobody can see me. My kit, by the way, is red tights, black mask, and 'Superlaaitie' written across my back in a lightning flash of yellow lettering.

Only Agnes knows my true identity because she washes my kit.

So off I fly to Mecca on my next international adventure.

When I get there the King is spitting at the ransom note as if it's a strip of bacon, vowing that, 'I'll get those infidels!' His wife is so upset that she faints. The King spots me as I alight in the courtyard of his palace and he rushes towards me. 'Please, Superlaaitie, you must help me. If you rescue her I will give you her hand in marriage.'

I fly all along the road following the tracks of the getaway car. It leads to the airport. When I get there a plane has taken off headed for the ancient Asian city of Ambetica. And, using my X-ray vision, I can see that the princess is on board, disguised and drugged to keep her quiet during the journey.

With my super breath I blow hard against one wing, forcing the plane to turn around and return to the airport. In no time I capture the abductors and throw them in a police van. And Princess Fathima is safe in the arms of her happy mother, Queen Tasneem.

Just as I take to the skies again, the King says, 'Superlaaitie! My daughter! She is yours now, have you forgotten my promise?'

I shake my head as I wave goodbye. The princess is a very pretty girl. She's got long black hair right down to her waist and looks just like Shireen who's in my class and smiled at me the other day. But you know what the people of Riverlea would say if we became girlfriend and boyfriend: 'Concentrate on your schoolwork first.'

My dad would say, 'Hey!'

ACTUALLY, THAT IS what my dad is saying right now! I'm sitting on our stoep with a comic in my hands. I've been daydreaming again and I've forgotten all about polishing my shoes.

In the meantime my baby sister Alison has been helping herself to the shoe polish and smearing it all over herself! She's got more polish on her face than I have on my Bata Toughees. And everywhere she goes – couch, armchair, table, lino floor – she's leaving behind a trail of shoe polish.

I look up at Dad in time to see his belt coming down at me – wham, wham, wham!

Jiga

In Colorado Drive there's a fish and chips shop, a grocer, another grocer, a dairy. To tell the truth, they all sell the same stuff give or take a fish and a chip.

It's here that the drop-outs of Riverlea gather, those boys who have decided to call it a day after only five or six years of schooling, whose fathers had said: 'You can read, you can write, you can count. That's enough. Go find a job.'

The boy found a job. He worked for three or four years. Then the boss closed down the factory and went back to Israel. Or the boy messed up one too many oak doors.

What do they do at the shops all day?

They watch and whistle at the nice, big schoolgirls.

'Hey, Charmaine. If those teachers hit you, you call me OK? Come sit here next to me and tell me what you learnt in school today.'

And when the girls aren't around to be teased, they turn on each other:

'Ou Tony, those left legs of yours, my bra. You can't wear Crockett and Jones shoes, you have to wear Crockett and Crockett.'

They brag about how much they used to earn:

'At Lucas I got four rand a hour, my bra.'

One of these shopstanders is Gerald Williams. But if your ma has given you that name she is probably the only one who is ever going to use it. All the Geralds in all the coloured townships end up as Jiga.

Jiga is married and lives in Zombie. He's got a low sense of self-esteem but high cheekbones.

Jiga's friends say:

'If it rains ou Jiga has to use two umbrellas.'

I doubt if Jiga has even one umbrella.

Nobody is spared from these street corner jokes, not even the elderly – the men who hobble about with sticks and the women who come shuffling two-by-two in slippers with a hole in them for a big toe to stick out. What spares some of these oumas and oupas from the barbs is that they are hard of hearing.

Marmaduke Aspeling is among a long row of loiterers sitting on the low wall. He stares at Ouma Vergie's big toe sticking out of her slipper as she hobbles by.

'Ouma,' he says, pointing at the toe, 'is Ouma taking the toe window shopping?'

Ouma Goodall is a hefty lady who has a bigger than normal nose. 'Vetkoek neus', the boys call her. She comes on her daily trip to buy a dose of snuff for herself and Tiger Toffees for her grandchild.

'Ouma Goodall,' Viccie calls out to her.

'Yes, my son,' she replies.

'Is Ouma buying snuff today?'

'Yes, my son.'

'I think Ouma should buy in bulk.'

Teasing is not these loiterers' only pastime.

'I know that one with the high cheekbones,' Agnes snorts.

'How do you know him?' I ask.

'Last week he grabbed Elsie's bag.'

Agnes tells me the story. The women all get off the train at Croesus station. They walk all the way through the veld to Riverlea, using the same route I take when I go to Coronation to visit my granny. Saturdays are payday for the housekeepers and that's when these loiterers waylay them in the veld and grab their bags and purses.

Last week Agnes's sister Elsie was walking alone when a man jumped out from behind a bush, yanked her bag from her and ran away while she stood there screaming.

Now Agnes and her friends walk to the station in groups of five, six or seven. And when I tell her the joke about Jiga and the two umbrellas, she doesn't laugh.

Short back and sides

After every five or six weeks our hair grows on to our ears and we look like those hippies from America who say, 'Cool, man' and 'Groovy' and take LSD and walk around in sandals.

Ma looks at us for a few days until she can't stand it any more. It's time for a haircut. If you want a haircut in Riverlea you go to Mr Barnes up there in Colorado Drive. On his gate a sign reads: 'Men 25 cents, Boys 20 cents'. That's right underneath the sign that says: 'Beware of the dog'.

The first time Derek and Shaune and I went there, I looked at this sign and it seemed like one was telling me to come in and the other was saying stay out. But we went in because we could see the two black and tan Alsatians, baring their teeth and snarling from behind a fenced-off enclosure.

Mr Barnes is fat with curly grey hair around the edges of his head and a bald patch in the centre. Instead of a belt, old-fashioned braces keep up his long pants.

He's from Swaziland and he has a kind of Swazi/coloured accent. He doesn't say 'this', he says, 'thees'. Instead of 'hot' he says 'hort'.

Once, while Mr Barnes was cutting my hair, I said to him, 'Mr Barnes, you have two Alsatians…'

'Ja,' he said, 'the best dogs in Riverlea, my boy.'

'But the sign on your gate says, "Beware of the dog".'

'So?'

'It should say: "Beware of the dogs".'

I can feel by the way the clippers have begun to move slower that Mr Barnes is thinking of an explanation.

'You know what I'll do,' he says. 'I'll get another sign and put it next to that one.'

We all laugh.

Mr Barnes has three haircut styles that you can choose from: schoolboy, short back and sides and smartboy. It doesn't matter which one you choose because they're all the same.

One day Derek gets onto the chair. Mr Barnes says:

'What will it be, young Nicky?' (He calls us all by our fathers' names.)

'Schoolboy, please Mr Barnes.'

Mr Barnes clips and snips, clips and snips. And just as he's about to remove the sheet, Derek says, 'Sorry, Mr Barnes, I meant smartboy!'

Mr Barnes steps back and says, 'How d'you like that, young man. It is a smartboy that I gave you – by mistake!'

It's nice sitting in Mr Barnes's yard on a Sunday morning, especially in summer. Mr Barnes is cutting hair, and the click-click-click can easily send you to sleep in the shade of one of his peach trees.

One or two men are sitting on kitchen chairs near him. They're not customers but drinking pals. Mrs Barnes is in the kitchen fewer than three metres away. She's cooking Sunday lunch and singing 'Abide with me' – the last hymn sung in church this morning. The grace of God is with her, as strong and wonderful as the dhunia floating on top of the slowly cooking chicken curry.

Little does she know that her husband is slowly getting nice and drunk, right here under her nose, in the shade of the kaalgat peach tree.

The bottle of Martell Brandy, the Coke and the glasses are hidden behind the dog's kennel in case Mrs Barnes pops her head out of that kitchen door to see what's happening in her backyard. Mr Barnes calls the brandy his medication. In this way he doesn't have to whisper when he wants some more. All he says is:

'I need some medication.'

One old man is reading the *Sunday Times* and every now and then the clippers stop clipping so that Mr Barnes can hear the latest.

Week after week the headlines are dominated by white people, either South African or American or British. But one morning the headlines are made by a coloured woman from Cape Town, one Pearl Jansen.

Each year South Africa sends its fairest maiden to take part in the Miss World contest. And of course, because apartheid is all about the colour of the skin and that skin can only be skin if that skin is white, only white girls are pretty.

One year the government decides, ja well no fine, let the blacks gather up their pretty ones and also have a sort of competition. Of course they can't call it the Miss South Africa contest because Miss South Africa already exists. How about Miss Africa South?

The pageant is held and Pearl Jansen, a coloured beauty from the Cape, is declared the winner.

Now South Africa has a Miss South Africa as well as a Miss Africa South. They both enter the Miss World contest. But the eyes of white South Africa are on the white girl, the pretty one. And ja, it happens. Neither wins. Both come in the top five. But Pearly girl beats the white one. And white South Africa is upset.

So, while I'm having my smartboy, I listen to the old timers. And when I go back home I go with more than just a haircut.

Broke

Ma and Agnes are always short of cash.

Agnes is so desperate sometimes that she asks me – of all people – to lend her five cents to buy a loose cigarette.

'Me, Agnes!' I almost laugh. I wish I could help her, but I can't.

Someone, her sister Elsie maybe, lends her ten cents. She buys a packet of Boxer tobacco and rolls her own cigarettes.

Every Monday we have to have money for school funds – twenty cents, and five cents for the Seaside Fund. Me, Derek and Shaune never have the money.

'But, Ma!'

'I don't have money,' Ma says. She takes out her purse, holds it upside down and shakes. A few pathetic coins come tumbling out, and spin on the table before they fall flat.

'That's for bread and condensed milk,' Ma says. 'If you can see more, for the Seaside Fund, take it. Or…' And Ma has an even better idea, 'Why don't yous just take this for the Seaside Fund and we'll all starve.'

We wouldn't dare.

The Seaside Fund is a fund from a collection of small change from all the coloured schools so that a dozen or so very poor children can go down to the sea in Durban for a school term so that they can get healthy and strong.

But they're just going to have to do without a contribution from the Van Wyk boys.

Sometimes Ma gets so broke that she doesn't even have a cent in her purse. She sends me to her sister, Auntie June.

'Tell her to please lend Ma a rand, just until payday.'

I go all the way to Lomala Street. Auntie June says, 'Ag shame, Chris. I don't have one cent—not one cent!'

'What do I do now?' Ma says, when I go back with the message.

Eventually, Ma does do something about being broke. She forms a stokvel with Auntie June, Auntie Louie and Auntie Pearl, all factory workers.

'What's a stokvel, Ma?'

She explains. It's a kind of club. Every week each member puts five rand into a kitty, which goes to one of the members—to be used for whatever she likes.

The next week they do the same and the money goes to a second member. And so on and so on.

'And then, Ma?'

'That's it,' Ma says.

I think about it for a while and I decide it's not going to help Ma get out of her financial problems. And it doesn't seem to help Auntie June.

Auntie June bought new linen for her double bed: winter sheets and summer sheets and pillowcases with the faces of the Beatles on them, all smiling, and with the words, 'I wanna hold your hand'.

'Imagine, Shirley,' she says, 'every night I cuddle up with the Beatles.'

Auntie June promises to pay the salesman ten rand a week for six months. But after seven weeks she loses her job and can't pay him.

'What am I gonna do?' she cries.

Ma can't help her because Ma's got this account and that account.

When the salesman knocks on the door, Auntie June tells her four-year-old daughter, Jessie, 'Tell the uncle I'm not here.'

'OK, Ma.'

In walks the salesman with his pens and his receipt book with the carbon paper sticking out.

'Hullo, Jessie girl,' he greets her because after six instalments he more-or-less knows the whole family. 'You wanna call your ma for me.'

'My mummy said I must tell you she's not here,' Jessie says.

'Where is she then?'

'In the room, Uncle.'

Auntie June is in the room listening to all this and she's thinking, why isn't there a deep hole in this room so that I can jump in it and fall all the way to Jerusalem and never come back.

Luckily for my auntie, the salesman realises that there is an awkward situation here so he says to little Jessie, 'OK, sweetie, tell your ma I'll see her next week, OK.'

Mr Jackets goes shopping
for shoes

Jeff Baadjes is a tall boy with an afro who lives at the bottom end of Flinders Street.

Agnes calls him Mr Jackets, because that's what his name means in Afrikaans. She finds this very funny. I discover later that, in Zulu, Agnes's language, there are surnames such as Ngwenya (Crocodile), Mthimkulu (Big Tree), Ndlovu (Elephant), and Mpisi (Jackal).

'So who's laughing now, Agnes?'

Agnes doesn't think these names are funny. I suppose you don't if you've been living next door to a Mrs Crocodile all your life.

Jeff Baadjes used to play football with us. But he dropped out of school and works in a factory and we hardly ever see him these days. One day I did see him getting off the bus.

'Heita, bra Jeff,' I said.

'Hey, I'm not your bra,' he said.

By this he meant that I was a kid and not one of his peers.

'So what do want me to call you?' I asked.

He hadn't thought about that and so he just clicked his tongue and walked on ahead.

Jeff is eighteen years old and he's been working for two years already after having dropped out of school in Standard Six (where he had been idling for a year or two).

Jeff wants to buy a pair of Florsheims. He would very much like a toney red pair because, he says, 'It will go kwaai with my light-

210

brown Mayfair Slacks and red Pringle cardigan.' Underneath that afro is a good head for colour combinations, no doubt about it.

Since leaving school Jeff has vowed that he will never read another book in his life again. Those dates in the History books – 1652 this and 1948 that... Those sums in Maths – divided by this and multiplied by that... Those pipettes and litmus tests... He's finish and klaar with all of that. And when he walked through the gates of Riverlea High for the last time, after having failed Standard Six again, he headed straight for the outskirts of the township, found an old mineshaft and threw the whole schoolbag down there – Kwa!

He got a job – thirty-three rand per week – as a forklift driver for Grit Aluminium Frames, a factory in nearby Industria.

During a Maths lesson Jeff's class teacher (ex-class teacher) Mr Green notices the empty desk.

'Where's Jeff?' he asks the class. The answer is multiple choice:

'He left, sir.'

'He's working, sir.'

'He says he doesn't like school any more, sir.'

'When did he ever like school?' retorts Mr Green with a sigh that blows a plume of white chalk off his collar.

'Do his parents know about this?' Mr Green wants to know.

'Yes, sir,' says Donovan January. 'His father got him the job at Grit Aluminium Frames.'

After a long pause Mr Green says, 'God help the coloured people.' He turns back to the blackboard (which is actually a greenboard), remembers something and turns back to the class.

'Who lives the closest to him?' he wants to know.

Marmaduke Aspeling puts up his hand. He's a fat pimply boy with left legs who does a lot of thinking in class – mostly about also leaving school.

'Go and fetch the textbooks from him,' Mr Green says. 'Tell him it's the property of the Department of Coloured Affairs. There's six altogether: English, Afrikaans, History, Geography, Mathematics and Biology. And I want them all.'

That evening Marmaduke goes over to Jeff's home. They sit in the backyard and share a cigarette and Jeff tells Marmaduke all about his newfound freedom: his adventures driving the forklift–which he's already nicknamed 'Forkie'–his boss, his workmates and his wages (to which he adds seven rand to make it a round and impressive figure).

Eventually Marmaduke tells him why he's here.

'Ah!' says Jeff. 'Ou Spoegbekkie sent you for the books.'

(Mr Green has a permanent drool, a blob of spit that loiters on the left corner of his lower lip. It has never turned into a trickle, but nor has it ever disappeared.)

'Tell him I threw it down a mineshaft.' Jeff has no doubt that Marmaduke–the king of gossips–will take his message, or a decent version of it, back to school.

'Huh! Did you really?'

'For sure. The same day I decided to chuck school.'

'So what do you want me to tell him?'

'Exactly what I told you.' Then Jeff has a better idea. 'Tell him the books are thirty-five degrees West and one hundred degrees down. He can go find it himself with that stupid compass of his.'

Marmaduke laughs and thinks, what a wonderful thing it is to be free of school and its teachers and prefects and principal, to be able to throw your books away and tell a teacher to go to hell on top of it. Only last week Jeff was trembling in the presence of canes, saying, 'I don't know the answer, sir', bending to take six of the best. But look at him now, blowing smoke rings into the night sky, driving a forklift all day, telling teachers to go to hell.

The next day Marmaduke reports to Mr Green–but leaves out the part about the degrees.

'Down a mineshaft?' Mr Green shakes his head slowly. He says: 'Well, at least it will stop Riverlea's kids from going to play near that mineshaft. Maybe we should get the Department of Coloured Affairs to throw books into all the dangerous places so that you kids won't go near them. They could put up warning signs that say: "BEWARE BOOKS HERE".'

THE KAYS OUTFITTERS clothing catalogue causes Jeff to break his promise about never reading a book in his life again. But, he tells himself, the catalogue doesn't have things in it that he has to memorise. All it has are things he wants: clothes. The catalogue is almost as thick as the Joburg telephone directory and page after glossy page is filled with male models posing in clothes – or kit, as it's called on the streets.

There are Arrow shirts, Pierre Cardin and Pringle jerseys and cardigans, Rex Trueform jackets, Mayfair slacks with a twenty-inch turn-up – and Hickok belts to go with them.

Don't talk about the footwear! There's Bostonian, Jarman, Florsheim, John Drake.

There's even a fashionable hanky. No self-respecting fashion-conscious drop-out will blow his nose into anything that does not say 'Pyramid' on the label. For a long time I want to know what a Pyramid hanky looks like, how it differs from an ordinary one. Then one day I get the chance. My uncle Mellvin takes out this big square dark green cloth, spreads it with a flutter and blows into it.

'Sies!' I say.

'Hey, sonny,' he glares down at me from his freshly vacuumed nostrils.

'Where did you get that ugly rag?'

'Rag! This is a Pyramid, my laaitie!'

After that I seem to spot them everywhere, draped over noses, hanging from pockets. They come in avocado green, boy scout khaki, and bitter chocolate brown.

Jeff takes the catalogue everywhere he goes: he 'reads' it on the bus, and at work he shoves it under his overall, goes to the toilet and pages through it there. Pictures run through his brain of himself in these clothes, strolling into a shebeen, watching a football match on Sunday afternoon, standing at the bus stop, bouncing down the road. Everywhere he goes there are eyes watching him, admiring him, adoring female eyes.

Since leaving school in March Jeff has got himself a new way of walking. It's a kind of bounce, as if the streets of Riverlea have been paved with rubber. It's a swagger that says to those who are watching: 'I know what's going on here, I know what you're thinking. Don't look for trouble with me.'

In December, Jeff gets his holiday pay. He picks up his friend Marmaduke (who is, miraculously, still in school) and off they go to town. Marmaduke has also adopted that bouncy walk although with left legs it doesn't look as cool as Jeff's. They bounce from shop to shop, looking out for bargains, comparing prices and smoking Consulate cigarettes. In Diagonal Street they look into the display window of Rex Outfitters. There's everything here: Arrow button-down shirts, Jarman shoes, Cutty Sark trousers...

'There!' Jeff says, stabbing a finger against the plate glass.

It's the Florsheim, resting on a little stand as if it's just touched down from heaven, having slipped off the foot of a fashion-conscious angel. It's toney red, and it's going for fifty-nine ninety-nine – a whole ten rand cheaper than Kays across the road.

Jeff is so pleased he throws an arm around his friend's fat neck and says: 'Check out this one. Same brand like Kays, same size, same colour. But look, it's a far better shoe than the Kays one, can you see that?'

'You're right,' Marmaduke nods, believing that there actually is a subtle difference.

And then Jeff explodes with laughter, and poor Marmaduke realises he's been duped.

'Gents.'

Jeff and Marmaduke spin around. It's a stranger, but a friendly and streetwise gentleman.

'I'm Phineas, from Soweto,' he says, shaking hands warmly with both of them. 'I work here for Mr Rex.' His black curls taper into a sharp point above his forehead giving him an eager, curious look. His smile reveals two rows of white teeth. 'Where you brothers from?'

'Riverlea.'

'Riverlea! I know a brother from there – Clyde Hobbs. You know Clyde?'

They don't know Clyde.

Jeff checks out his attire, and approves. Phineas looks like he's getting good discounts from his boss: he stands, not too tall but proudly, in two-tone John Drakes, black pants are held around a slim waist by a snakeskin belt with a shiny silver buckle. A check shirt, black and white, fits in nicely with the trousers and shoes. Phineas is a man with style.

Phineas takes out a packet of Rothmans, flips up the lid with a thumb, taps the box deftly – and out pop exactly three cigarettes. He offers them to his new friends and helps himself to one.

A match appears in his hand. Jeff pats his pockets to find his matchbox, but there's no need – Phineas lifts his left John Drake and lights the match with a quick scratch. He lights up for all of them and takes a deep draw.

'Just tell me what you want,' he says. 'I'll get it for you below wholesale price.' As he makes this offer wisps of smoke drift out of his mouth.

Jeff is impressed, by the offer and the man's smoking prowess. He points at the shoes.

'Ah, that one I can get for you easy,' says Phineas. 'For thirty-five rand straight.'

Jeff's eyes jump and he swallows the smoke in his mouth too sharply and coughs.

'But…' Phineas makes a movement with both hands, as if he's polishing an imaginary ball. 'You know what I mean?'

Of course they know. Actually Marmaduke doesn't know, but he sees Jeff nodding. Actually Jeff also doesn't know but he sees Marmaduke nodding.

Phineas says: 'I'll get it for you.' But he needs time. 'Twenty minutes, wait for me outside Koh-I-Noor.'

Koh-I-Noor is the jazz record bar where Duke Ellington's 'Perdido' is making all the Saturday morning shoppers click their fingers.

Jeff and Marmaduke bounce off to Koh-I-Noor and stand underneath the giant neon sign of the silhouetted trumpeter blowing away a tune. They take in the aroma of the curry balls from Kapitans.

'You smaak some curry balls?' Jeff asks his friend.

'That will be grand.'

'I'll even buy you a twenty – after I pull this deal.'

'You'll have enough change after you give Phineas the thirty-five rand.'

Jeff nods his head slowly. 'Thirty-five rand. No-no-no. Thirty rand is all he's getting.'

'But he said thirty-five.'

'What he says and what he gets is two different things.' He takes thirty rand out of his wallet and shoves it in his top pocket. 'Just zip and watch closely.'

Another jazz melody fills the air with a brightness that changes the mood of the morning.

'Cannonball Adderley!' Jeff declares, kissing the air.

It's actually Miles Davis blowing 'My Funny Valentine'.

As the melody trails to its sad and beautiful end they see their man Phineas making his way through the crowds. He's clutching a parcel, newspapers wrapped around a box. The other hand touches the tip of his Ayers cap. He looks less cool now than before, looking over his shoulder three times before crossing the road. He reaches them, looks around one last time.

'You got the thirty-five rand?' he asks.

'I got thirty,' says Jeff.

'Aw now!' Phineas doesn't like this.

'I'll bring the balance next Saturday,' says Jeff.

'You taking me for a one,' says a disappointed Phineas. But he nevertheless hands over the parcel and takes the money.

'Toney red?' Jeffs reminds him.

'Ja, that's what you said.'

'Size eight?'

'For sure.' He turns on the heels of his John Drakes with a quick reminder that, 'You owe me five.'

'Sure chief. Next week.' Jeff has the box in his hands and as Phineas vanishes into the crowd he mutters, 'Go and ask your mother for the five.'

Marmaduke chuckles.

Jeff unwraps the parcel. Sure enough there's a shoebox, a

Florsheim shoebox. And it says 'Size 8' and it says 'Toney red'. He removes the lid and…

'Look!' Marmaduke gasps.

There aren't any toney red Florsheims, but in their place cabbage leaves are tightly crammed into the box. This is a perfect gift for those hamsters that some of the richer boys keep in cages in their backyards. But it's not what bra Jeff ordered.

Jeff runs here and there looking for the conman in the Ayers – through crowds of shoppers, in a stinking public toilet, in shops.

'There!' he says, pointing at a cap with a man underneath it. A thick crowd of slow walkers separates them but Jeff is making his way up to the man.

'He's far too short and too fat,' Marmaduke observes.

'Hey!' Jeff calls out to the man. He's not Phineas.

'I'll get him, I'll get him,' Jeff raves. 'I'll get the mother, my ma hoor my!'

He turns to Marmaduke. 'But did you see how I tricked him with that five rand? I knew he was up to something, I tell you I just knew it!'

He looks away and quickly wipes a tear with his Pyramid hanky. He turns to Marmaduke, clutches his wrist. 'Hey, this is just between the two of us OK?'

'For sure.'

But Jeff knows, and his poor heart sags at the thought, that by Monday afternoon the whole of Riverlea will know the story of Phineas and the Phantom Florsheims.

In the meantime, both Jeff and Marmaduke seem to have lost their famous bounce.

Good books and bad books

All the Christians in Riverlea have a Bible in their home. Ours is black and on the cover it says 'The Holy Bible'. The Afrikaans-speaking Christians have the Afrikaans Bible. On the cover it says simply 'Die Bybel'. They haven't bothered to include the word 'Heilige'. As far as they are concerned, it's 'the Bible' and you don't have to say anything more.

On Sundays all the churchgoers can be seen on their way to church with a Bible under their arms. The Ebenezers, the Catholics, New Apostolics, Anglicans, Dutch Reformed…

In church the pastor or priest tells them where he's reading from today: it could be Genesis or Joshua, Exodus or Psalms, Ruth or Revelations. Some find the verse quickly, others too late, others just open on any page because they can't read.

The priest reads and reads until he comes to one sentence that he wants everyone to remember for the rest of the day – possibly for the rest of their lives. He usually repeats the line about three times, each time in a different way:

> In **my** father's house are many mansions. If it were not so I would have told you.
>
> In my father's house are **many** mansions. If it were not so I would have told you.
>
> In my father's house are many mansions. If it were not so I would have told **you**.

I sit three rows from the front between Derek and Shaune. Derek is peeling a scab off an old sore on his wrist. Shaune looks totally bewildered by all these mansions.

I think it means that there's a place in heaven for all of us. But this priest is saying, not so fast. When the Lord speaks, He speaks in riddles.

After an hour and four hymns and the taking of the collection, he comes out with it. It really does mean that there's a place in heaven for all of us.

The other famous quote that means exactly what it says is this one:

The devil finds work for idle hands.

Ma and Dad put things on top of their wardrobes. These are things stuffed into shoeboxes and thrown up there so that we won't go and scratch around in them. But over the years, the piles grow larger and higher and ever more irresistible. And then the time comes when a boy can't help himself.

A perfect time to scratch is in the afternoon between three thirty and five o'clock – after Agnes has left and Ma is not yet home from work.

I won't give away Ma and Dad's secrets, except to mention two things I found up there.

The first thing was the death certificate of my brother Alistair. It was an ordinary, folded-twice, government-looking document that was stuck there between two other documents.

I was going through everything quickly, just glancing at things and putting them aside, looking, I suppose, for something interesting. And trying to do it before Ma came home. Then I found it. It was a folded government document with English on one side and Afrikaans on the other. In my haste I almost put it on my 'Seen Already' pile, when my eyes caught the words: 'DEATH CERTIFICATE'. Those words, written in capital letters, are bound to give anyone a fright – especially a boy on a wardrobe who's doing what he's not supposed to, when normal boys and girls are outside in the sunshine playing games in the street.

After 'NAME' a government official had written in my brother's name in blue ink on the long dotted line: 'Alistair van Wyk'. There was also: 'RACE', 'CAUSE OF DEATH', 'DATE OF BIRTH'. So this is what the clerks at the Department of Births and Deaths did the whole day: filled in the particulars of dead people on dotted lines.

I wish I hadn't found it. It was like a speed trap, just lying there between other folded papers – an old water and electricity receipt and a handwritten recipe for ginger beer, waiting for me. And now I couldn't go on with my 'work'. I took hold of it and sort of slid down the side of Ma's wardrobe and onto her bed. Sitting on the bed with my knees up, I begin to read it word for word.

He was born on 6 June in the morning and died on 6 June in the evening. My ma once told me how it happened. He was born in my ma's bedroom in Newclare. A nurse, Miss Moosa, delivered him and Mrs Sacks, our next-door neighbour, was there to help. Miss Moosa had sent my dad out of the house, and he went to sit in the Sacks's kitchen where he smoked two cigarettes and waited.

When he was born, Mrs Sacks went over to my dad, 'Come, you have another son. Congratulations.'

The first thing my dad said when he looked at Alistair was, 'Why is he so blue?', more puzzled than alarmed. Because of the blueness, he probably had not noticed that the baby had his pitch-black curly hair.

'Sometimes they do look like that just after they've been born,' Miss Moosa said. But she did seem a little concerned. And then she made a decision. She wrapped him in two large towels – he had already been named as Alistair, handed him to my dad, and as she did all this, told Ma:

'He needs an incubator. I'm taking him up to Corrie hospital (which was less than ten minutes away in her car) and you'll hold him while I drive,' she said to Dad. And off they went.

Alistair died at the hospital ten hours later, from a brain haemorrhage.

And that's his whole life story.

Now, perched on Ma's bed, I start to wonder what he would have looked like. Would he still have had dark hair or Derek's light curls, Shaune's dimples? He was born a year after Derek but a year before Shaune. So, if he were alive right now, he would've been going around with one of them. Or maybe the three of them would've hung out together.

And his voice – how would that have sounded? I imagine him coming into the bedroom and saying my nickname.

I don't know how much time must have gone by while I sat there on the bed. It must have been about eight years, because that's how old he was when I stood back up on Ma's bed and put my brother back on the wardrobe where he could go on gathering dust.

Alistair was safe 'in the arms of Gentle Jesus' Ma always told us. But not me: I was about to embark on my next misadventure here on Earth. And this is how it began.

I was about to bring my scratching to an end – finding Alistair had been enough for a whole week of scratching and, as they said in the *Kyk* and *See* photocomics, I was emotionally drained.

Then I saw the Holy Bible.

It lay hidden under a layer of dust. Not a thick enough layer to hide it or hide the words embossed on its cover. I blew off the dust, coughed, slid off the wardrobe once more and began to examine this Bible.

It wasn't the one we took to church. This one had covers of bright red leather. It had a zip running down its three sides. You could unzip it, read a verse or two, and zip it up again.

Whose Bible was this? I found the answer on the blank page opposite the cover where the owner had written:

Thelma Petersen
(followed by a Coronation address and)
Johannesburg
South Africa
Africa
The World

Thelma had done this to make sure that if ever her treasured Bible was lost, it would be brought back to her by some Good Samaritan. But, poor Thelma – here was her Bible hardly six kilometres away and no one was bothering to return it to her.

I put it back on the wardrobe, but that, sadly, was not the end of the story of the Bible.

A WEEK LATER, me and the guys are walking home from school, kicking stones and talking nonsense. There's Rathead, Hippie, Crowbar and Marlon.

Marlon has to learn a Bible verse – John 3 Verse 16 – for orals the next day. He says he knows it already and recites it for us all to hear:

'For God so loved the world that he gave his only forgotten son…'

'No no no,' I stop him right there.

'What?' Marlon asks.

'It's wrong.'

'What's wrong?'

'It's not *for*gotten son it's *be*gotten son.'

He looks at me as if I'm mad or something. Then he gives me that shove on the chest that your friends give you when they're a bit annoyed with you. It doesn't quite make you topple over but it does make you stumble backwards.

'How much bet?' I challenge him.

'I'll give you two comics if you're right,' he says.

We clinch palms and Rathead chops our hands apart to officially seal the bet.

We get to our house and I tell him to stop right there – 'by the gate' – while I go inside to fetch the Bible.

I know I'm going to win this bet, but I don't think I'll get any comics from him. We hardly ever honour bets. But just knowing that I was right is enough reward for me – besides, he's my friend and I'm helping him pass his orals.

'What's wrong now?' Agnes wants to know.

'The Bible, Agnes. Where's the Bible?'

She shrugs and turns away—I suppose she has those eggs to lay and chickens to hatch. I can't find our family Bible. And then I remember the other one. I get it off the wardrobe and rush out the door, unzipping it as I go.

'Nice Bible,' says Marlon as I flick to John in the New Testament and show him 'begotten'.

I wait for him to call it a misprint or something, because that's how Marlon is. But he gives me a slap on the back and shakes my hand. He says, 'I owe you two comics.'

'Ja.'

Later, I'm getting ready to go out and play, when Marlon pitches up, with a really good pile of comics under his arms.

'I owe you two,' he says. 'Choose.'

It's hard to choose only two when there are so many. I choose a *Superman* and a *Spiderman* that look almost brand new. For the rest, Marlon wants to know if I have any to swop. I don't. In the meantime, he has become distracted by the red Bible that is lying on the dining room table. He unzips and zips it again, remarking how 'awesome' it is.

'Really, really awesome,' he says.

I watch my friend admiring the Bible and a plan begins to form in my head.

'You like that Bible?'

He says he likes it very much.

'I'll swop you all those comics for it.' There must be about twenty-five in the pile.

He looks at me and says, 'You serious?'

'I am,' I nod. 'We don't really use that one.'

He marches out of our home hastily, before I can change my mind, leaving me with *Archie*, *Superman*, the *Fantastic Four*, *Spiderman*...

'No homework today?' Agnes remarks, with a sarcastic lilt in her voice, as she dusts the furniture around me. I ignore her—Spiderman has better things to say.

When Ma gets home from work, we throw her a quick glance and a 'Hullo, Ma' and it's back to Superman, Archie and Mickey

Mouse. Derek's on the couch, Shaune's on a kitchen chair, I'm lying on a bed.

Ma keeps having to say: 'Put that down and go to the shop for me,' or 'Leave that now and go throw these peels in the dustbin.' But otherwise Ma's happy to be left to her own thoughts and her cooking.

Ma finishes the cooking, Dad comes home. He pages through *The Star*, we eat. All the usual Van Wyk routine.

After supper the routine changes. Instead of listening to the radio in the lounge, Ma and Dad go and lie down on their bed with a handful of comics each. I can hear them chuckling away at the stupidity of Sad Sack, Mickey Mouse and Donald Duck.

But somehow, somewhere between Sad Sack and Bugs Bunny, Ma realises that I have much more than my usual fare of comics. She must've got that light bulb in a speech bubble above her head that comic book characters get when they get a bright idea.

'Where did you get these?' she asks.

'I swopped them with Marlon.'

'How many comics did you give him?'

I never thought this would come up, the ins and outs of comic swopping. Next my parents will be asking me if I found anything interesting on the scrap heaps or which Simba chips flavour was Vino's favourite.

'I didn't have any comics to give him.'

'So then… what did you give him?'

'You know that Bible that was on Ma's wardrobe?' I try not to look at the stupid wardrobe as I say this.

'The Bible? You swopped the Bible?'

I nod and lick my lips. Right now I could do with a glass of cold water.

Dad sits bolt upright. He doesn't say anything but I can see a thought bubble poised above his head too – about to explode into four-letter words.

Ma and Dad exchange looks and she says, 'Can you believe this child?'

Dad says, 'What Bible?'

Ma says, 'The zip-up one.' She's irritated with him because while she's into anger phase, he's still lagging behind at confused phase.

'The red zip-up one?'

'Yes, Nick, what other zip-up one is there?'

'Jesus Christ!' says Dad, quoting from the New Testament. 'What the hell did you go and do that for?'

'What did you want on my wardrobe in the first place?'

Questions are flying at me and I don't know who to answer. But it doesn't matter because I don't know what to say.

But that night as I lie in bed feeling sorry for myself I know that actually I do have something to say. But if I had said it, well, that would have been the end of me, that's for sure. Lying in bed, with the advantage of stillness and darkness, I work out my response and it goes like this:

'I have been your son for many years, and for all of that time we've had a Bible in the house. But not once have I seen you open it and read it. But I bring a few dozen comics into the house and you lie on your bed as if you're on holiday, reading them and laughing out loud.'

And then I fall asleep.

Penpals

One day my friends and I can't talk of anything but football and cowboy movies. And the next thing we're talking about nothing but girls.

I'm almost fourteen years old and I would really like to have a girlfriend. But it's not easy.

Conos isn't scared of girls. He gets onto his bike, rides past them once or twice, gets off his bike and says, 'Hi, aren't you Janet?' She says, 'Yes, why?' 'I know a Janet from Newclare,' he says. 'She's pretty.' He looks up and down the street, and then straight into her eyes, and adds, 'But not even half as pretty as you.'

Janet clicks her tongue and says, 'Haai, I'm not even pretty!' But her face has gone red and she seems pleased.

'D'you mind if I park my bike here against your fence for a while?' Conos asks.

'It's OK,' she says. Shyness has made her voice a little squeaky.

And so they have a chat about general things. About his family and hers, which teachers he likes and which ones she's fond of. About his favourite subject and hers. About his star sign and hers.

He plays with the handlebars of his bicycle. She makes a semicircle in the sand with her shoe, mostly looking downwards and avoiding eye contact.

Then Conos decides that it's time for the second, most important question. 'Do you have a boyfriend?'

226

'A boyfriend,' she says, and laughs.

'But do you? I'm serious.'

'Of course I don't.'

'Will you go out with me?'

A few small schoolkids pass them and one of them greets her. She waves back, happy for the distraction. But my friend is persistent.

'Will you?'

'My father will never allow me to have a boyfriend,' she says.

At this point Conos knows he's in with a chance. Her father might not like it but she herself is OK with it.

'But it will be our secret,' Conos says, lowering his voice a little.

But even for Conos with his wavy locks and handsome face, and cockiness, and flashy racer that he built up himself from the parts of a dozen different bikes, even for Conos love is not immediate.

'I'll give you the answer tomorrow,' she says.

VINO AND I don't have the guts to do this. I don't even have a decent bike. And if I did have one, the last thing I'd do is lean it against a pretty girl's fence.

Vino went on holiday to Cape Town last Christmas, and he came back with interesting girl statistics.

'Here in Joburg there are two boys for every girl,' he says. 'But in Cape Town there's ten girls for every boy.'

'Serious?' Conos asks.

Philip, a lanky boy who grows a thick moustache during school holidays, says: 'In Cape Town I lived in Athlone with my cousins. I tell you, every time I walked down the street, girls whistled at me!'

One afternoon, after Agnes has listened to her radio serial, I say, 'Agnes, have you ever been to Cape Town?'

'Of course!'

'Really? When?'

Once upon a time she worked for a white family in Parktown North. One Christmas the family – mother, father and toddler twin girls – motored down to Cape Town for their annual holiday by the sea. Agnes went with them to look after the girls.

'They took me everywhere they went, shopping, to the beach, places like that. And in the evening when the madam and baas go out I look after the girls.' She sweeps dust off the front stoep. 'It was a nice holiday for me.'

'But you were there to work,' I remind her.

'But still it was a nice time.'

I want to ask her about the coloured girls, but I have to do it with 'style' otherwise I won't hear the end of it and Agnes will be teasing me from Monday to Monday.

'I hear there's a lot of coloured people there.'

'Too much!'

She's almost done with her sweeping. I have to ask now, but I can't think of a way.

'A lot of the men, they don't have front teeth.' She laughs. 'Why?'

'Agnes, how should I know?'

She stamps the dust out of the broom. I have to ask now, before she disappears into the house with that 'Eggs to lay, chickens to hatch' farewell of hers.

'Does it makes them look ugly?'

She shrugs and says she doesn't know.

'Are there lots of coloured girls?'

'Too much.'

'Pretty ones?'

'Pretty ones,' she assures me.

'Prettier than Veronica McKay?'

'Some are like Veronica, some are more nice.'

'How many pretty ones did you see?' I can't seem to stop myself now.

'Too much.'

'More than ten?'

'More than a thousand!'

'How old are they?'

'All sizes!'

She laughs and lifts the broom and tries to spear me but I jump out of the way. 'One day when you get married you can go to Cape Town and get a wife there.'

'But then I'll have two wives.'

'What you mean?'

'You said one day when I get married…'

She doesn't wait for the rest of it.

'And I'm not interested in girls anyway,' I call as she disappears into a bedroom.

THERE'S A CAPE Town based newspaper that finds its way into the local café in Riverlea every Thursday. The *Cape Herald* is a coloured newspaper, about the doings of the coloured people in Cape Town. About a new coloured school being built in Elsies River and a newly promoted coloured school inspector called Mr February. About the parades of the Coon Carnival on Tweede Nuwejaar and the death of a famous Imam. There are stories about coloured jazz bands and rock bands, coloured weddings and coloured soccer results.

I dream of going to Cape Town. A chosen few in Riverlea have been there and returned with tales of wonder – about Table Mountain, flat and half-hidden in a cloud, and the blue ocean. And the pretty girls.

This is a place where some dads take their families. The Van Wyks' dad, however, has neither the money nor the wherewithal. He has never taken us to a movie or on a picnic twenty kilometres from dreary Riverlea. So Cape Town might as well be off the coast of Mexico – even though, ironically, Dad was born in Cape Town.

But the *Cape Herald* has a Penpal column, and this is a way to get to know girls (or goosies, as the Cape Town boys call them). I'm going to get myself some pen goosies, I decide. I write down my name, address and hobbies:

> *reading* (Absolutely true, but I don't emphasise it because girls don't really like boys who read all day.)

music (True, although I prefer Uriah Heep and Mott the Hoople to Showaddywaddy and the Mamas and the Papas.)

sport, especially football (Girls love a football player even if he's as thick as a brick. There are guys in Riverlea who can dribble themselves past half a dozen defenders, but can't spell 'goal'.)

Star sign: Cancer (This is a requirement.)

I wish to correspond with girls between the ages of fourteen and sixteen.

Two weeks later, I buy the *Cape Herald* and there it is under the Penpal column, one square inch of me! It's a funny feeling seeing my name in the newspaper, telling the world I love books and want girls! I am convinced that the entire South African nation – or at least all the coloureds – have opened the *Cape Herald*, quickly paged to the Penpal section, run a finger down all the names, stopped on 'Chris van Wyk', and said, 'Aha!' This is so embarrassing.

But once the embarrassment subsides, I start checking our letterbox five, six, seven times a day. This penpal thing doesn't really work, I decide. But it does.

A week later I got – all the way from Cape Town – not one but three letters. From Myrtle (Libra), Ursula (Scorpio) and a Soraya (who hasn't given her star sign, but there will be time for all that). The next day there's another three. A day later, two more and the day after that, seven! I now have fifteen letters from thirteen different Cape Town girls (two of them have already written again asking why I haven't replied).

I had hoped for five. In the end I am writing to about fifty girls.

Agnes is very interested in this new development in my life. And I share it all with her, reading out bits from the letters.

'Look at this one,' I tell her. 'See how she makes tiny little circles above the i's.'

'It looks nice,' Agnes says, stamping the broom in excitement.

'Look, Agnes. This girl's handwriting is exactly the same as mine. When I opened the envelope I thought she had sent my letter back to me.

'Aha!' Agnes says. 'Same-same.'

'Agnes, this girl says…'

But Agnes has just heard the time on the radio. 'Hoo!' she wails. 'Tomorrow is a busy day. I got eggs to lay…'

I GOT AT least two letters a day every day, and mostly three or four.

Every evening, after doing my homework (or sometimes instead of doing it) I reply to every letter. I describe my family – mother, father, sister and brothers, my friends Conos and Vino. I tell about my teachers, the ones that I like and the ones that I don't. I describe Riverlea with its yellow minedump and its row upon row of exactly-the-same houses, and its yellowish, dusty people.

Sometimes I write dialogue, tucking actual bits of conversation between inverted commas, just like they do in the novels:

I showed Conos your photo. He said, 'Hey, that's a beauty! Gimme her address.'

'Oh no,' I said, shaking my head.

They write about their townships and teachers and families, their dreams to become a teacher, a doctor, a famous singer. They write in English and Afrikaans, and sometimes in both languages in one letter. They write on perfumed paper, on sheets with butterflies and flowers fading into the background.

One afternoon when I come from school, I check the letterbox, but it's empty. I make sure, bending low, looking closely, putting my hands in and feeling the sides and the roof. Instead of the usual three or four letters, there's nothing. I'm not too bothered by this though. Agnes often checks the letterbox before I get home, and she might've taken out the letters already.

I go inside. Agnes is in the kitchen. She has slices of bread lined up in rows and she's smearing butter and jam on them.

'Hullo, Aggie.' I sometimes call her this when I need something from her – in this case, letters.

'Hullo.' But she barely glances at me and carries on smearing and slicing.

'Did the postman come today?'

'Aw, but he comes every day.' She still hasn't looked up at me.

'How do you know?'

'There's a letter for your father.'

She's right. I see a brown envelope addressed to N.C. van Wyk. It's an account of some sort.

Agnes pours five cups of tea and calls us all to 'Fetch'.

In the room I change into my everyday clothes. I go back into the kitchen to have my lunch and, what's this on the kitchen table? It's a white envelope addressed to Chris van Wyk. 'Agnes?'

'Oh I forgot,' Agnes says with a click of her tongue. 'That one also came.'

'Are you playing the fool with me?' I say, making a fist, but she darts out of the room.

I sit down in the dining room and read my new letter from a thousand kilometres away – slightly delayed by Mrs 'Eggs to lay' from Soweto. And now she interrupts me by calling from the kitchen:

'What's the time there?'

It's my turn to click my tongue. I stop reading about how my friend Janette from Bonteheuwel went up Table Mountain and glance up at the clock – but I can't see the clock because there's a letter in front of it addressed to me!

From the kitchen comes a familiar chuckle.

'You got time to play hey, Agnes?'

I'm reading letter number two when Agnes appears in the lounge – and strolls out again, leaving an envelope on the table.

In the end Agnes's joke consists of a total of five letters.

Sweet Stephanie

Whilhile I was looking for girls far away in the shadow of Table Mountain, one or two were looking for me, right here in the shadow of the minedump. This is how it happened.

Like most boys, Conos and I wanted things that we (meaning our parents) could not afford. Things like wristwatches, caps, jackets with the peace sign on the back, racers that came with little water bottles, even ice-cream cones with the flake inside instead of just the ordinary one.

'Do you see money growing on my back,' both Ma's said when we asked them for more than twenty cents, or, 'What do you want to do with so much money?'

So Conos and I get an idea in our heads to generate our own wealth. Actually the idea is in Conos's head first and he puts it into mine one day when we're dragging our poor selves up Flinders Street.

'Let's start a business,' Conos says.

'What kind of a business?'

'Selling sweets.'

The idea is not original. There are three shops in Colorado Drive, all of which sell sweets. And then there are at least twenty different house shops spread all over Riverlea, selling sweets, ice blocks, tamaletjie and popcorn. In fact, as Conos makes the suggestion we stroll past Mr and Mrs Laing where the buttery aroma of new popcorn floats past our noses.

'All we need is some capital,' Conos says.

When he says 'capital' I stop slouching and begin to walk upright; it's not every day two boys walk up dusty Flinders Street using such fancy words.

'Just about a rand each,' he explains. 'We go to Chapelat (the sweet factory in Fordsburg) to buy our stock. In no time we'll be laughing all the way to the bank.'

I'm impressed. It sounds like Conos has been doing a business course.

About a month later, we're on a Putco bus, our capital in our pockets (actually it's all in Conos's pocket because he's the boss), to buy stock, and hoping to eventually laugh all the way to the bank.

In about two months' time we'll add a few more business terms to our vocabulary, such as 'insolvent' (a sad result of mothers borrowing from the profits to buy bread, Agnes borrowing for train fare, and theft by siblings). But for now, everything is going sharp-sharp.

Chapelat is like walking into a giant sweet. You smell toffee, then Romantics (those tiny pink sweets that you're supposed to suck before you kiss your girlfriend), then that chewing gum flavour, then those crunchy beetle nuts. And then you see all these sweets in giant, sticky, crunchy sizes.

We buy big boxes of beetle nuts, toffees and mints. If they were for us, they'd last a couple of months. But this is the beginning of our sweet business.

Back in Riverlea, we halve the stock. Conos takes his share home and I take mine.

Ma gives me jars for the sweets and a little saucer for my float.

Agnes helps me run my branch of the business when I'm at school. During the mornings business is slow, mostly pre-school kids coming to spend the cents their grannies and mommies have given them. The main business happens after two o'clock when all the kids are back at home.

On a good day there's a knock on the back door (the front door is out of bounds after Agnes has polished and shone the stoep) every five minutes.

'Two cents Sharps.'

'Five cents beetle nuts.'

'Three cents Chappies.'

I can hardly do my homework properly. I write three words and it's knock-knock, another two words and knock-knock-knock.

My friends come to buy – Hippie, Rathead, Crowbar. And even the neighbours I don't know so well – boys and girls from down the road in Colorado Drive and Galana Street. In fact, one of my best customers is Stephanie. She's my age, also in Standard Six, in an Afrikaans class at school.

I sit at the kitchen table so that I can be close to the door. Agnes is washing dishes.

Knock-knock-knock.

I open the door and there's Stephanie in her yellow school gym, socks with grubby ankle smudges and school shoes. Her frizzy hair is combed down flat according to school regulations, with an elastic band holding together a tail at the back. Her eyes are big and shiny and pretty.

She says, 'Hullo.' I say hullo back. She buys two cents beetle nuts, with a five-cent coin.

My beetle nuts are four for a cent. (The shops give you three for a cent but Conos said we can give four because our overheads are lower.)

She holds out one hand. I count out eight beetle nuts for her, jiggling them out of the bottle.

A beetle nut looks like a little brown beetle and its inside is packed with peanuts. They're all the same size, but every now and then you come across a small one, the runt in the litter. One such runt slips out of the bottle and into my customer's hand.

'Sorry.'

'It's OK.' She giggles.

'You sure?'

She nods. But I don't think it's fair and I drop another one into her hand. 'You can have that small one as pasella.'

'Thanks,' she says. 'He's like a little baby.' She glances at the books on the table and says, 'Are you doing homework?'

'Ja.'

She looks closer and murmurs, as if she's already begun to suck a beetle nut.

'What's it?' I want to know.

'Your handwriting is so nice.'

Before I can react to that she turns and disappears out the back door.

Agnes must surely have something to say about that. I glance at her, waiting for a remark. But she seems lost in packing away dishes. And she's even humming the hymn 'How great thou art' – which she often sings in Zulu.

After two customers – and only three more sentences of my comprehension assignment – there's a knock and it's Stephanie again. This time she's wearing a red and green dress with straps on her shoulders. The elastic band that was tying her hair down is gone now and it's bouncy and fluffy.

'Hullo.'

'Hullo.'

Agnes is still in the kitchen, wiping a cupboard.

'Tiger toffees,' Stephanie says handing me a two-cent coin.

I give her four toffees.

She doesn't leave immediately. Instead she smiles at me and I don't know why. Then she says, 'Look here.' And gently unfolds a tissue in her fist. It's the small beetle nut.

'Our baby,' she says. I feel my face go red because I know Agnes is listening to every word.

'I know all the books of the Bible off by heart,' Stephanie says.

I'm so happy that she's changed the subject that I ask her to recite it for me. She says she's shy, but goes for it.

'Genesis, Exodus, Leviticus, Numbers, Deuteronomy, Joshua, Judges, Ruth…'

She really is shy, moving her feet and holding on to the doorhandle as if she's about to fall over. And on and on she goes, not pausing between Old Testament and New:

'First John, Second John, Third John, Jude, Revelations.' She exhales and looks at me proudly.

If she left out a book or two, I wouldn't know, but I'm sure she didn't. I tell her it's amazing.

'I won a prize for it.'

'A prize. Where?'

'Bible school.'

'What did you win?'

'A Bible.'

It doesn't make sense to me. If she knew all the books of the Bible, surely it means that she had a Bible already. And what would she think of me if she ever knew what I did with spare Bibles!

'OK goodbye,' she says, skips out of the house and is gone.

I go back to my homework. The kitchen is quiet, and Agnes is still singing her hymn. I'm relieved – she hasn't noticed a thing.

But then, still packing dishes away, she changes the words of the hymn and I hear:

'Now Chris is shy
because he's got a girlfriend.'

I look up and glare at her. But she doesn't even glance my way, pretending that she really is singing the hymn. But Agnes can't suppress a laugh for long, and she laughs.

'She likes you,' she says.

'Who?'

'Who, who? That one.' She points to the door, where Stephanie's perfume still lingers.

'Stephanie?'

She nods.

'Agnes, Agnes, Agnes.' I swirl my forefinger against my temple.

'I'm not made, I know what I see.'

'Just because she buys sweets from me and talks and jokes with me…'

'Ten times a day: knock-knock. Who's there? Stephanie. Knock-knock. Who's there? Stephanie.'

'Two times today, Agnes, not ten times.'

'And I see you've given her a little baby.'

I click my tongue. 'That was just a joke.'

'She's clever. I see she knows all the Bible names.'

'No, we're looking for a name for our baby.'

She knows I'm messing around, but she asks, 'What are you going to call him?'

'Deuteronomy.'

She laughs. I pretend to be my father, rise up from the chair and call: 'Deuteronomy! Come here! What did I tell you about cleaning this yard!'

Agnes slaps her thigh in delight.

'She's coming again today…' She looks at the clock on the kitchen dresser. 'Before five o'clock.'

The next day Agnes confronts me:

'Did she come again yesterday?'

'Did who come?' I ask, not looking up from my novel.

'Don't waste my time,' she says. She grabs my book out of my hands so that I will be forced to look at her. Immediately I grab my Biology textbook and pretend to read that. But I can't hold out for too long and I blurt out the truth.

'She came, she came. She bought two cents beetle nuts and she told me I've got nice teeth. Are you satisfied?'

For months after Stephanie, I look in the mirror trying to see what Stephanie has seen. And then I make sure that nobody's nearby and I say to the Chris in the mirror:

'Hey sonny, Stephanie likes you.' And I give myself a wink.

Dear Sir, please excuse Christopher

Sometimes on a Monday morning, Agnes comes to work a little drunk – or with a heavy babalaas.

She doesn't have to tell me, I can see. The usually chirpy tongue is heavy today, the eyes are half-closed with thick dark rings around them. The spring in her step is gone and she slouches from room to room picking up clothes, dusting a cupboard, sweeping.

'Jo,' she groans, rubbing her beret around on her head. 'You got Grandpa?'

I laugh at this: Agnes asking me to whip out a packet of Grandpa headache powder on request.

'So where in Soweto was the party?'

She turns her head slowly to focus on me.

'No eggs to lay today?'

'Today I kekeleza,' Agnes confesses.

It means to pretend that you are working while in the throes of a severe hangover.

When Ma comes from work she senses that it was not the usual efficient Agnes who had been cleaning up that day: a room doesn't look properly swept, clothes haven't been ironed…

Ma calls me. 'What happened here today?' she asks.

'Where, Ma?'

'Here-here-here. This house wasn't cleaned properly today. Was Agnes OK?'

'Ja, she was OK.'

AGNES RETURNS THE favour when every once in a while I can't face going to school.

For example, the Woodwork teacher Mr Stanley wants my toothbrush rack ready for inspection today, complete with its stupid little holes for five toothbrushes and its little shelf for the toothpaste tube. All I have to offer Stanley so far is the plank that he gave me at the beginning of the term.

Maybe I could ask him to give me at least a mark for neatness.

The problem with these teachers is that they want to make all the jokes. As soon as you say something funny, they glare at you and say: 'Sonny, you trying to be funny or something?'

There is also that Biology homework that I didn't do – it's all about ions and stuff and I don't know what the hell is going on there.

So today I decide I have the runs. I have no such things but I shall write the following letter, as close as possible to Dad's handwriting, which I shall present at school tomorrow:

Dear Sir/Madam
Please excuse Christopher for not attending classes yesterday.
He apparently ate some contaminated food and as a consequence suffered from a bad case of diarrhoea.
Yours faithfully
N.C. van Wyk

I've become so good at forging letters that I do it for my friends too. I've done a couple for Tommy Isaacs after he ran out of ideas. All his letters used to read: 'Please excuse Thomas for not being in school yesterday. He had to attend his granny's funeral...' Until Mr Goliath said to him, 'Thomas, how many grannies do you have left?'

'YOU GOT A SKYF?' I ask Agnes.

I began smoking when I turned fourteen.

'When did you start?' I ask Agnes.

'Also when I was about fourteen,' she says. 'Everybody start when they fourteen.'

I laugh because I don't agree with her, but I'm in no mood to argue. Agnes takes out a stompie and lights it. She takes a few drags and gives it to me.

In actual fact I started smoking *properly* only a few weeks ago. Conos and I were strolling down Colorado Drive at about eleven at night. That's the best time to smoke because all the mothers and fathers are fast asleep, including your own.

We'd been smoking for a month or two and now Conos turns to me and says, 'You're wasting the cigarettes.'

'What?' I ask, leaving an indignant cloud of Rothmans floating out of my mouth.

'You're not swallowing the smoke.'

'How the hell can I swallow the smoke?' I'm a little cross now. What's he trying to say? That I'm a laaitie, that I can't smoke. But Conos doesn't want to argue, he wants to help.

'Watch,' he says. He takes one long drag that makes the cigarette glow brightly.

'Hey watch it!' I warn him. 'That's so bright the people can see from behind their curtains who we are.'

He explodes with laughter and the smoke flies out of his mouth.

'If you want me to show you how to do it you have to stop making jokes.'

'OK, no more jokes.'

Another deep drag, and then he sucks in.

'Swallowed,' he says, but his voice is like a ghost's. Then it all comes out in a sharp stream.

I try it.

I cough like hell.

I try again.

I cough.

I try one more time.

My head spins a little. Aah! I'm hooked on cigarettes.

But now there's a problem. I need my fix every day. At least three cigarettes per day in the first three months, to increase by about one cigarette every month until it reaches twenty.

So back to the problem. I get about thirty cents a week pocket money and I need about two twenties per week. My Maths is useless, but I can work out that I've got a problem.

The only thing I can do is steal cigarettes. I steal from Ma's Van Rijns. When she switches to Rothmans I have to change my brand too. Dad smokes Gold Dollar, a cigarette so strong it's theft proof. One puff and you're dead. It might be this stuff that makes him swear so much.

All evening I watch the yellow box of Van Rijns and wait for an opportunity. Ma doesn't let it out of her sight – not because she suspects a thief lurking nearby. She just always has the cigarettes within reach. On the dining room table when she's chatting to her visitors or listening to the radio, on the kitchen table when she's cooking, on the bedroom dressing table when she's reading.

But then she gets up to go to the loo. And that's when I make my move.

Tommy Isaacs told us the other day he stole a cigarette from his Ma's pack and she found out.

'How did she know there was one missing?'

'She had two in the pack.'

AFTER I'VE SHARED the stompie with Agnes, I go outside and tie some wire around the gate to stop anybody from coming into our yard. Agnes sees me doing it, but she doesn't ask any questions – she knows why. If you play truant too often your teacher sends a posse of boys to fetch you. Ask Kevin Baadjes about that.

Kevin is a slim, good-looking guy who decided that his future was in music – to be specific, playing the lead guitar in a Beatles-style pop group. Riverlea High fell far short when it came to fulfilling Kevin's music education needs.

Music lessons consisted of a Mr Jacobs arranging us all in a semicircle in the front of the class. With his cane he pretended to be a famous Viennese conductor and got us to sing:

Oh Beulah Land
Sweet Beulah Land
As on the highest mount I stand
I look away
Across the sea
Where mansions are
Please pray for me

So Kevin played truant at least once a week, practising his chords at home.

His class teacher Mr Jackson sends four big boys to fetch him. They creep into the yard down there in Gironde Street. They hear the guitar somewhere inside the house as Kevin is strumming away. And they hear the unmistakable voice of Kevin, singing so beautifully that for an enchanted moment they forget why they're here.

But then they remember again. They creep up to the kitchen and peep in. And they behold the strangest sight.

Kevin, in very colourful pyjama shorts, is posing with one bare foot on a kitchen chair. He's strumming away and singing to a heavy-set lady, their housekeeper Gladness:

Oh Gladness
When I look at you I feel such sadness…

Gladness, for her part, is ironing away looking neither pleased nor displeased by the colourful and talented troubadour.

BEING AT HOME during school hours is like being an intruder in another world. Everything is unfamiliar. The housekeepers hang washing outside in the yards and you can hear them chattering away to each other across the fences. A Beauty shouts to an Agnes, an Elsie calls out to a Gladness, a Sophie gossips with a Martha.

Then there's the radio. I turn it on and listen to white people playing Bingo!

If it's not Bingo time, then it's *Hospitaal Tyd* a music request programme for white people in hospital. '*Daar's 'n lied en 'n glimlag vir jou,*' I find myself singing along to the signature tune. '*Dis Hospitaal Tyd onthou*' (There's a song and a smile for you. It's Hospital Time remember).

When two thirty eventually comes, I go over to Kendrick Patel, a classmate, to find out if I'm in trouble. I choose Kendrick because he's the closest to my home. He's one of those boring guys who never stays out of school.

There's quite a few of them, boys and girls. At the end of the year they always get that Attendance Certificate, awarded to students who did not miss a single day of school. And usually the Attendance Certificate is all they get, while other students, who were absent for a few days, get awards for English, Afrikaans, Biology, Maths, Science and Geography.

Attendance Certificate! What a stupid idea. I think if you came home with such a certificate only, your father should give you the beating of your life because you were at school every day but your classmates who were not there all the time, got all the awards.

Counting words

Agnes is ironing. We don't have an ironing board so she throws an old rug over the kitchen table and does her ironing there.

I sit right by the table watching her, feeling the heat of the iron, listening to the iron sizzling over the damp spots of the clothes.

The iron is like a boat sailing across the cotton, smoothing the waves. She sprinkles on more water and the iron goes ch-ch-chhhh.

'Agnes, can I ask you something?'

'Ja.'

'Is your mother still alive?'

'Uh-uh,' she shakes her head. 'She's late.'

I think about this while I watch the iron gliding into sleeves and over collars.

Agnes asks, 'Why you smiling?'

I did not realise I was smiling.

'I tell you my mother is dead and you smiling.'

'I'm not smiling because your mother is dead.'

'Then why?'

'Because you said "late".'

She looks at me sharply and I realise I'm not making any sense.

'In English you can say, "the late Mrs Dlamini". But you can't say, "Mrs Dlamini is late". Do you see what I mean?'

She doesn't say yes, she doesn't say no. All she does is slide the iron across a shirt. I try a different angle.

'Let's say the trains didn't come again today and instead of coming to work at seven you arrive at eight o'clock. So my mother comes from work and she sees some of the work isn't done. She asks me why and I say to her, "Agnes was late today." You understand, Agnes.'

No response.

'Agnes.'

She gives me a withering look and says, 'I wasn't late today.'

ONE DAY CONOS comes to visit, as he does almost every day. He and Agnes know each other well, and if she's made us our bread and jam, she gives him some too.

Conos is a 'housechild' and she hardly ever gives him a second glance after they've greeted each other. But today, Conos has come with magic.

He shows us two squares of cardboard the size of a book. The boards are attached to each other by a flat red ribbon.

'What's that?' I ask him.

'Magic.'

'Show me.'

That is exactly what he's come to do. He flips open the two boards.

'Put your pen underneath the ribbon,' he says.

I place my pen under the ribbon.

'Are you watching?' he asks.

I nod.

He slams the board shut, opens it immediately. My pen is still there – but not where I put it. It's tucked under the ribbon on the right-hand flap!

'Hey, that's cool!'

Agnes wants to see too. Conos shows her and she squeals with laughter.

When Conos himself disappears she says, 'He's a clever somebody.'

'You mean a clever *person*, Agnes.'

'Why can't I say "somebody"?'

I look at her, wondering. Like 'late', it's going to be too hard to explain.

'Because it's just wrong,' I tell her, but she's not even listening. She's gone to fetch washing off the line.

ONE DAY, I'M playing truant again, sitting at home with Agnes. We're sharing a cigarette at the kitchen table, and I say to her:

'Teach me Zulu.'

'You want I must teach you Zulu?' She seems surprised.

'Ja.'

She shakes her head and I ask her what's the problem.

'You supposed to be at school learning there, but you stay here with me and I must be your teacher – and I got work to do!'

I see her point.

'OK, Agnes, do your work but teach me to count from one to ten. I'll follow you around the house.'

And so there we go from room to room. From the kitchen:

'One.'

'Kunye.'

'Say it again.'

'Kunye. Coon-yeah.'

'Two.'

'Kubili.'

'Kubili.' I follow her to the lounge. And I say:

'Three.'

'Kuthathu.'

Into Ma's bedroom.

'Four.'

'Kune.'

'But isn't that "one"?'

'No. One is coon-yeah. Four is coon-eh.'

'Jislaaik!'

'Jislaaik what?'

'They don't make it easy for those of us who were not born in Zululand.'

Agnes laughs. 'They made Zulu for Zulus,' she says.

247

'Come-come, Agnes we don't have time for jokes. Five.'

'Kuhlanu.'

I repeat, 'Koo-Shla-noo.'

Into our bedroom.

'Six.'

'Isithupha.'

'Seven.'

'Isikhombisa.'

Now we're back in the kitchen.

'Eight.'

'Isishiyagalombili.'

'Oh no, Agnes!' I hold my hands against my temples in mock pain and walk about in a small circle.

She laughs. 'Is it too long for you?'

'Aw, Agnes, isn't it too long for you too? For all the Zulus in the world?'

She laughs again, and this brings out my funny side.

'If I ever go into a shop in Zululand, there in Natal, and I want to buy eight sweets, you know what I'll do?'

'What?'

'I'll buy four sweets twice. Kune and kune again.'

'Then you will never buy nine,' she says.

'Oh! Here we go. What's nine?' I pretend to close my ears.

'Isishiyagalolunye.'

I say it but leave out a syllable or two.

'And ten?'

'Ishumi.'

After my lesson, Agnes tests me and I fail, scoring a miserable kubili out of ishumi.

'It's too hard, Agnes,' I shake my head. 'Too hard.'

'Make us some tea, and then I'll show you an easy way to learn.'

Ten minutes later, we sit down at the kitchen table sipping our tea.

'So show me then.'

She asks me to lay a hand flat, face down on the kitchen

table. 'Like this.' Beginning with my pinkie, she starts counting in Zulu until she has reached my thumb, kuhlanu. She takes my other hand, and this time starting with the thumb, she continues counting:

'Six is isithupha. And it's the Zulu word for thumb.'

'Are you serious, Agnes?'

'I am,' she nods, and continues:

'Seven – isikhombisa…' She holds my seventh finger. 'Meaning "the finger that points".'

I look at my pointing finger in wonder, as if noticing it for the first time.

'Eight is isishihiyagalombili and it means "leave two behind". Nine is isishinyagalolunye and that means "leave one behind". And ten is ishumi and ishumi means: "we have a group".'

AT SCHOOL WHERE I'm supposed to be, the bell goes off – it's time to change periods – from Afrikaans to Biology, English to Domestic Science, Business Economics to Geography…

I'm not part of that world today. But the sun is shining on my face.

'Agnes!'

'Yebo!' she shouts back.

'What is sun in Zulu?'

'Langa! Why?'

'It's shining on my face.'

And I'm happy.

The day they came for me

It had to happen. When you play truant a few times you don't realise how often you're doing it. If somebody had asked me how many times a month I was staying away from school, I would've said, 'Ag, about twice a month.' The answer was more like four or five times a month. You don't think anyone is taking notice, but your class teacher is recording it all in that big book of his – the attendance register.

At about eleven in the morning there's a knock on the front door.

Agnes holds the iron in mid-air and says, 'Who?'

'They've come to fetch me, Agnes.'

'Who?'

'Schoolboys.'

She says, 'Why?'

'What d'you mean why, Agnes?' I go and open the door, hoping that I'm wrong. In walk Humphrey, Gordon, Errol and Tokkie, all smiling stupidly as if I'd been on the run for months and at last, they've tracked me down.

Gordon says, 'Get your schoolbag. Mr van Rensburg says we mustn't come back without you.'

'Do you mind if I get dressed first?'

Humphrey (his nickname is Humps but I'm not going to call him anything today) steps forward and hands me the twist of wire that I used to keep the gate closed. The others think it's a big joke.

I leave them in the lounge to comment on and giggle softly about the things we have in our lounge: family photos, my dad's football trophies, seashells and a picture of horses on the wall. Nothing is spared.

I make sure to brush my teeth to get rid of the cigarette smell. I put on my uniform and grab my satchel and off I go with my escorts, down Flinders Street and across the football grounds to Riverlea High with half the day gone.

We don't say much because this is not an ordinary stroll with one's buddies. This is a posse that is about to deliver me triumphantly to Mr van Rensburg.

Something about the posse amuses me despite my unhappy situation. They're walking in a deliberate formation: Humphrey's in front of me, Gordon and Errol are on either side and Tokkie's taken up the position behind me. This is to prevent me from escaping – which I have no intention of doing.

If I fled towards the railway lines Humphrey would be on top of me before I ran a metre. He just happens to be the fastest under fifteen sprinter in the school – despite his plump body and short legs. Van Rensburg could've sent him alone and let the others get on with their schoolwork.

Then there's the flanker Errol, as untidy as Humphrey is quick. His school blazer has fatty blotches all over it, his grey pants have dark marks around the pockets, his shoes are desperate for a dab of polish.

His fingers are oily. Don't ever shake his hand for any reason – you'll get the oil!

Errol's ma gives him vetkoek for lunch two or three times a week. This is a grand lunch if you think that most of us get ordinary sandwiches and some get nothing.

Errol's vetkoek are stuffed with mince curry when his ma's got some money to spare. Sometimes dhal curry, left over from last night's supper. Then there's vetkoek and apricot jam – which is not bad at all – when his mother's a little broke.

A vetkoek is not called a vetkoek for nothing. All vetkoek learn to swim even before they are born – in hot oil.

Look around on the playground and you can see who's been eating vetkoek for lunch. It's all those with shiny lips and cheeks.

Even the lunch packets that litter the playground every day have strong evidence. The shiny ones that glow had vetkoek in them.

So you have to have style to carry a vetkoek around with you and not stain yourself. Errol doesn't have style. He never has a hanky so his face glows all day – in the mornings in anticipation of his lunch, and in the afternoons after lunch.

Sometimes he doesn't think about what he's doing and then he slips his lunch into the same compartment where his books are. Mr Smith chances upon this big, shiny blotch that lies across a double-page spread of a map of the tropics.

'What's this?' Mr Smith bellows, casting a shadow over Errol's desk almost as big as the vetkoek stain.

'A vetkoek stain, sir,' Errol mutters, licking his lips.

And Tokkie is a short boy who looks like he should be in primary school. He's got about seven or eight sisters and brothers, older and younger than him, all as short. His father is short. His mother is short.

They all have wavy hair in either copper coloured, bronze or red. They stick it down with thick dollops of Kamillen hair cream and this gives them a garden gnome look.

'If yous each stand still in your garden it looks like a picture from "Snow White and the Seven Dwarves",' somebody told poor Tokkie once.

According to a reliable source Tokkie's entire family are a very excitable lot. 'You go to their house up there in Medway Street. You knock on the door. Somebody says, "Come in!" You open the door and step inside – and you trip and fall over the entire family – mother, father, sisters, brothers, the whole happy lot of them. Because they're all so eager to see who their visitor is, they all come running to the door.'

MR VAN RENSBURG didn't cane me that day. He just warned me: 'See that you're here every day.' But it was too late. I failed and had to repeat the year at school.

Janine

One day at school I fall in love. Luckily for me, I'm not a heavy smoker yet or my poor heart would have stopped from the shock.

It happens like this: it's about quarter past twelve on a Wednesday afternoon. Vino and I are walking towards the boys' toilets. After this break are the final three periods of the day: a double English followed by one Business Economics. We've got our homework for both teachers so there's no worries. Besides I like English a lot so I'm in a good mood.

The schoolground is a swirl of blue blazers, white shirts, blue ties and yellow skirts.

Every second boy and girl is singing that new pop song that's just come out. It's by a band called Dr Hook and the Medicine Show and the song is as bizarre and quirky as the band. It's about a guy who's just broken up with his girlfriend. He's feeling remorseful and maybe he wants to make up again, so he phones her. Her mother answers and:

Sylvia's mother says Sylvia's busy,
too busy to come to the phone.
Sylvia's mother says Sylvia's happy,
so why don't you leave her alone.

It's sad, but it's also funny—just like that story of the lorry that fell into the hole.

Vino and I are singing the song too, walking along. It's a nice hot day at the beginning of February, and summer is still going to be sticking around for a while. Vino and I have just begun our first term of Standard Seven.

An ice-cream vendor is passing ice-cream through the school fence. The less fortunate are sucking Lekker Lollies at two cents a throw from the dairy nearby.

We pass the netball court where there's always a treat waiting for a teenage boy – when the girls jump high up, it's not the ball that catches your eye.

We're still singing when we turn the corner. I see her and go quiet. And I stop.

'What?' Vino says and looks to where I'm looking – and laughs.

'Who is she?'

'Janine.'

'How do you know?'

'Aw! Because it's her name.'

Suddenly I realise what a heavenly name Janine is. Janine. Jerneen. Jehneeen!

Janine is standing and chatting with three friends – Hilda, Bernadette and Sophie. I know all of them and Hilda is in fact in our class. I see them, but my brain deletes them immediately – like multiple choice answers in an exam.

Janine is taller than all of them. She has big brown eyes, long black hair, long legs. On her left cheek is the prettiest mole I've ever seen on a cheek.

They're having a good chat about something or the other; Hilda says something, then Bernadette, Hilda again, then they all speak at the same time – and then they laugh. There's a lot of gesturing, pointing with the fingers, flicking of fringes (in the case of Janine and Sophie – the other two don't have flickable hair).

Vino and I pretend we're having a chat, but we're watching them. Every now and then one of them looks our way. But the gossip is juicy it seems, so it's only a glance and back to the story.

Janine has the least to say. I like that – it obviously means she's cool, composed, and knows how to behave in public.

She glances our way. Then she reaches into her inner blazer pocket, brings out a little pink comb and proceeds to comb her hair.

Aha! Could she be combing her hair because I'm watching her? It's possible.

Vino pulls me away. He tells me she's in the other Standard Seven class. Her class teacher is Mr Meier.

'Why the hell isn't she in our class?'

'It's better like that,' Vino says. 'What if you get something wrong and the teacher shouts at you? I wouldn't want my girlfriend to be in my class.'

'You're right,' I nod. But I think there's another reason. Vino's got a stammer. It's th-th-this and tha-tha-that all day long. But I don't mind. He's my buddy and I don't finish his sentences like some stupid people do, and as far as I'm concerned he's OK.

'I'm glad Ronel isn't in our class,' he says.

Vino's been in love with Ronel since primary school and Conos and I are the only ones who know about it. Ronel herself is blissfully unaware of the love for her that keeps Vino tossing and turning in bed like that guy in the song by the Ivy League.

Our Afrikaans teacher Mr Kalk gets us to read out loud for a mark. Poor Vino, a dozen words takes him the best part of five minutes while the entire class waits.

The other place where Vino stammers a lot is at the café – especially when there's a crowd of people waiting to be served. One day his ma sends him to buy a tin of sardines. The shop is a bit busy and Vino and I are having a chat while he's waiting his turn. Suddenly we hear, 'Next!' It's Mr Klink and he's looking at Vino and Vino panics. 'What you want?'

'I-I-I…'

'Bread?' Klink says.

'N-n-no…'

'Milk?'

'No, I…'

'Cheese?'

Eventually Klink isn't asking, he's just packing stuff onto the counter: polony, cigarettes, biscuits…

Vino turns around and walks out of the shop and all I can do is follow him. Klink wasn't doing that because he was impatient, he did it to get a laugh. And he did, from his stupid assistants and one or two shoppers.

So you can imagine if Ronel were in our class.

In the toilet I look at myself in the mirror.

'Ah no!'

'Whatsit?'

I show Vino the two new pimples on my forehead, fat and glossy. I pop them out and dab my forehead.

Vino spots a big blackhead on his chin and sorts that one out between two fingernails.

'You notice how smooth her face is?' I ask Vino.

He nods.

And then there's that mole.

DOUBLE ENGLISH MEANS seventy minutes with Mr Garson. I like English and I like Mr Garson with his thick glasses and his woolly, untidy brown hair.

All the teachers go around calling each other 'Sir' or 'Meneer'. These are people who drink together – tea in the staffroom and alcohol in each other's homes. But in front of us they pretend that they are merely associates.

That's why it's nice to hear Mr Garson call out to Mr Johnson, 'Howzit, Davey!' Or to Mrs Radcliff, 'Gloria, so how did it go at the wedding?' From time to time Mr Garson says something none of the other teachers would dare say: 'Apartheid is a sin! It's filth!'

Mr Garson always has a surprise for us. And today is no different.

'Quiz Time!' he announces. There are four rows of desks which make up team one, two, three and four.

I shift about excitedly on my seat. I never miss the radio quiz programmes: *The Quiz Kids* (where white schools do weekly battle) – I find that I am at least on a par with these kids; *The Surf Show 21* (also white contestants) – I answer every third or fourth question; *Test the Team* (listeners send in their questions to four extremely clever white men, professors or doctors) – I can never answer any of these.

Mr Garson is quizmaster and scorekeeper. With chalk in one hand and questions in the other, away we go:

'Who is the author of *Prince Valiant* serialised in the *Sunday Times*?'

Me: 'Hal Foster!'

'Who said: "I have a dream"?'

Me: 'You, sir, and Martin Luther King.'

He chuckles, and then he's the serious quizmaster again. 'In which country was the 1966 World Cup played?'

Debbie: 'Mexico.'

How the hell did she know that?

'Who wrote *Jock of the Bushveld*?'

Trevor: 'Jock.'

'No.'

Firoza: 'Sir Percy Fitzpatrick.'

'Who said, "She loves me yeah, yeah, yeah"?'

Vino: 'The Beatles.'

'Who is Clark Kent?'

Me: 'Superman.'

'In America they're called astronauts, in Russia…'

Me: 'Cosmonauts.'

Our team wins and Mr Garson congratulates us. Desiré, a plump girl whose father owns the local butchery, says: 'Sir, next time put Chris in our row,' and she blows me a kiss. I look around in Hilda's direction, hoping that she will tell Janine what happened in Quiz Time today.

Two days later, there's a knock on the door. Mr Garson says, 'Come in.' My head is buried in an H.G. Wells short story.

Vino gives me a jab in the ribs and says, 'Look who's here.'

It's Janine. Vino and I sit in the front row and right now I am closer to her than I have ever been. The eyes are sparkling

257

today, the mole is still there, still perfect. The legs are still long and shapely.

She goes up to Mr Garson and murmurs in his ear while he nods away. He says, 'Class, listen up.'

The buzzing subsides and he says:

'I'm sure you all know Janine Jacobs. Janine do you know some of these faces?'

'Yes, sir,' she says, much too shy to look at any of the faces now.

Janine is your new classmate. Janine, go and find a place somewhere.'

One or two boys shout, 'Here Janine, next to me!' But Janine seeks out her buddy Hilda.

Vino is whispering in my ear, 'Hey, sonny, just what you wanted!'

I whisper back, 'Shhhht', because I'm scared somebody might hear him.

How did this come about? Simple. The girls in 7B do Geography and History. The girls in our class, 7A, do Needlework and Domestic Science. Geography and History are all about monsoons and tropical climates and the French Revolution; both tough subjects. Needlework and Domestic Science are about sewing on a button and how to cook a delicious bredie.

Janine wants to do Domestic Science and Needlework, the easier subjects. I don't mind at all. I have a picture in my head of us happily married one day. I arrive home from a very stressful day at the office. I am tired and demoralised. In this dream I am not a writer but a bigshot in some office – thanks to all those love story comic books that I gobble up together with *Superman*.

I stagger through the front door and the heady aroma of sirloin steak in a French sauce bubbling away lifts my spirits right away. And that mole on the face of my wife in that apron!

'Look at you!' she says. 'Shirt hanging out again, and a button missing.' She whips out her sewing kit right there and then and before I can say 'Holey moley', I look and feel like new.

I tell Vino or Conos none of this. Every now and then we

have a little verbal skirmish and this is enough ammunition for a full-scale war.

VINO AND I watch Janine every day – actually I watch her and Vino eyes Ronel. And every day I learn another little thing about her.

She has only one slice of bread each break, that's two per day, and she doesn't eat butter because it's fattening. In her inside blazer pocket there is of course the pink comb. In the outside top pocket where the monogram is stuck, she has a quarter square of cloth neatly cut from a yellow duster. Every break without fail, two minutes before the bell rings, Janine takes out this duster and carefully buffs her shoes.

She wears her hair in two different styles. Sometimes she lets it loop onto her forehead and back again behind her ears. Or she combs it all back and holds it in place with an Alice band – a blue one that matches her blazer or a yellow one that goes nicely with her skirt.

Vino and I can't see enough of our 'girlfriends'. After school we take a walk past their homes, just to see if we can spot them. Janine lives all the way up there in Kentucky Street. Ronel lives in Bushdove Street near T.C. Esterhuysen Primary School.

Sometimes we're lucky and we get a glimpse of them, sometimes we don't. The nearer we get the more anxious we become. We make sure we're looking presentable and that our shoes are clean.

'D'you think I have pigeon toes?' I ask him. Mrs Milton once called me pigeon toes because I accidentally kicked a ball into her yard and it missed her head by a millimetre.

Vino looks down but says he can't really tell. We're about to pass the shops and there are dozens of kids milling around and we want to be discreet about these things.

'I tell you what,' he says. 'You make like you're tying your shoelace and I'll walk up ahead. And then I'll watch you come on.'

Vino's verdict is that I don't have pigeon toes. And nobody has spotted our piece of research.

It's like that afternoon when we were on our way to Vino's house to listen to his new Grand Funk LP. We're having a chat about something or other. There's a trio of four- or five-year-old boys squatting in the dusty pavement playing cars. As we walk past them, Vino laughs out loud at a joke that I make. His mouth opens wide giving the boys a worm's eye view of his dental arrangements.

One of the kids says, 'Sies, jy't muistandjies.' (Shame on you, you have mouse teeth.)

I can't believe what I've just heard! Vino is almost fifteen years old. Most seventeen year olds would never dare say that to Vino and this little thing hasn't even been to school yet. Vino grabs him by one of his twiggy arms and lifts him high into the air. 'Must I kill him now or tomorrow?' he asks me.

The little thing is kicking and screaming and warning, 'I'm gonna tell my mommy!'

'Let's see now,' I scratch my chin, playing along with Vino. The boy's buddies are very concerned about the sudden turn the afternoon has taken. One of them has forgotten to sniff up the snot on his lip. 'Kill him tomorrow.'

'You make sure you here two o'clock tomorrow so that I can kill you OK,' Vino tells the boy. 'Will yous make sure he comes on time?'

One of them nods. 'I will, Uncle, my ouma got a watch.'

For weeks after that, especially if we're going to pass by Ronel's house, Vino wants to know from me if he really has mouse teeth.

'Never,' I reassure my buddy.

One afternoon, just as we pass Janine's home, the door opens, she comes out and stands on the stoep. My heart goes boom-boom. I say:

'Oh no!'

'Just act natural,' he says. But I don't know what 'natural' is: do I look at her, do I look away, do I pretend Vino and I are deep in conversation and haven't noticed her at all? In the end I don't look at her. I've come all the way up here hoping to catch a glimpse of her – and I don't.

Every day my heart aches with a sadness that Janine has still not noticed me – despite my rapid-fire Quiz Time answers, despite my witty jokes that make even Mr Garson chuckle. She seems more interested in her pink comb and her square of yellow duster.

Time to make a move

One afternoon, while Agnes is preparing our lunch, I get an idea.

'Aggie.'

'Ja.' But she doesn't look up.

'I wanna ask you something important.'

'Ask.'

'But I want you to look at me, I don't want you cutting bread and…'

'I'm late today, today I'm behind. You can wait for tomorrow or you can ask while I work.'

'How do I tell a girl that I love her?'

She laughs out loud, so much that she has to put the knife down and stop working.

'Oh, you haven't got time to help me but you got time to laugh at me!' But I'm laughing too.

She says, 'Sorry,' and wipes tears from her eyes. 'Say again?'

'How do I tell a girl that I love her?'

She ponders, smears apricot jam onto a slice of bread.

'But you say it every day.'

'What do you mean?'

'Those letters that you write to those girls in Cape Town.'

'Agnes, Agnes,' I click my tongue. 'I don't tell them I love them…'

'You do. You show me their photos, you tell me which one is nice, which one is not so nice, which one you favour.'

'OK, I give you the benefit of the doubt.' That's a new expression I picked up from Mr Garson the other day and I use

262

it about five times a day. In a week I've given about two dozen people the benefit of the doubt. 'But what I want to know is, how do you ask a girl straight out, face-to-face.'

'Ah! Ah! Ah!' she says, backing away from the bread board with each ah. 'You love someone.'

I knew this was coming and I'm prepared. 'No.'

'You are, I'm not stupid.'

'Agnes, I'm writing an essay, like a story – for school. About how a boy and girl fall in love. My teacher will give us marks for it.'

She gives me a sceptical look and hands me a sandwich.

'I'm serious.'

'Do you know beads?' she asks.

'What?'

'Beads.' She gestures by first putting both hands around her neck and then one hand around her wrist.

'I know what beads are. What about them?'

'Did you ever see a woman wearing beads?'

'Yes.'

'Where?'

'Mostly in pictures, but sometimes also in real life, in town.'

'What kind of beads?'

'Necklaces and wristbands.'

'Now I'm asking you one question,' she says pointing. 'Only one.'

'OK.' Agnes is funny even when she tries to be serious and I try not to laugh.

'Were these women in love or not in love?'

'Agnes!'

'Married or not married?'

'I forgot to ask them, maybe next time I see them…'

'You don't have to ask them nothing,' she says. 'The beads talk.'

She begins to tell me a fascinating thing: that, in Zulu custom, lovers use beads to declare their love for each other. If a Zulu man is working in the mines far away in Johannesburg and he wants to tell a woman in his home village in Natal how much he loves her, he sends her beads. The different colours – blue, green, yellow, black and white – all stand for different emotions and moods: love, faithfulness, heartache, anger, longing.

I listen, enthralled, to all this, until she breaks the spell suddenly with:

'Hey, I have eggs to lay, chickens to hatch.'

I don't know why I thought Agnes could help me. Beads. As if Janine is a Zulu girl from somewhere in Zululand, living on the banks of a river, balancing a pot on her head. But it serves me right for not being brave enough and telling Agnes the truth.

IT'S APRIL! THE first school holidays have arrived. We've written exams, but we get the results when we go back to school in two weeks.

Vino and I are sitting in their dining room listening to Uriah Heep and, as usual, we're talking about Janine and Ronel. We don't speak about them when Conos is around because he's getting more and more irritated with us.

'What's wrong with you guys?' he says. 'Just go up to the girl and ask. If she says no, ask another one.'

Maybe Conos is right. And there and then I decide that, like Elvis says, 'It's now or never.'

'What do you think?' I ask Vino.

'Look, she can't kill you. She can say yes or she can say no, but she can't kill you.'

'OK, this is how we do it…' I tell him my plan and he agrees. It works like this: Vino has become a little friendly with Hilda and she borrowed his Carole King *Tapestry* LP. So tomorrow he takes his bicycle and goes up to her house. He tells her look, Chris is in love with Janine, he wants to be her boyfriend. Can you go and tell her and ask her to think about it and give him an answer.

'Tomorrow afternoon,' Vino says.

'Tomorrow afternoon,' I stamp a fist on the table. 'But wait. What if Janine tells Hilda to tell you to tell me to not be a coward and come and ask her myself?'

'If she says that then the answer will for sure be yes.'

'You think so?'

'I know so.'

I give him the benefit of the doubt.

The afternoon comes and there I am, leaning against our gate. I look down both ends of the street, looking out for the red racer of one Irvin 'Vino' Conway who today will bring me good news or bad.

I look around while I wait for the answer. For the first time in my life I start thinking seriously about the state of our yard.

There are two kinds of gardens in Riverlea. Beautiful gardens with lots of flowers and lawns and hedging. The Starkeys up there in Colorado Drive have such a lovely garden that they were even featured in the *Rand Daily Mail Extra* (the special edition for coloureds and Africans). The caption said it all: 'The Starkeys of Riverlea show off their first-prize garden'.

Then there are the lousy gardens with a flower here and there, begging for a drink of water, dying.

We have neither, because we do not have a garden. All we have is a row of hedging growing along the fence, and a peach tree where we buried our dog Bruno. Otherwise we have a desert. The Kalahari in miniature.

We tried once or twice to make a garden. Ma planted a few rosebushes and some lawn. But it didn't last. Despite endless promises to Ma and Dad we never watered the garden, we never dug up around the flowers. And in the end we turned the place into a playground for ourselves and our friends.

But now I look around and I'm thinking: if Janine says yes, then we'll be going out – going steady, as they say. And that means that she might come around here once or twice a week to come chat and listen to my heavy metal records.

Well, I can't have Janine walking across this desert. She'll have a fit! Remember she's got that yellow duster that she keeps taking out to wipe her shoes. No, I think I'll start on a garden as soon as Vino brings the good news. I'll put some more hedging between ourselves and the Vergies on this side and the Edwards on that side. Flowerbeds along the hedging. A path of flat stones from our front gate up to the stoep. Extend the stoep a little so that you can put a bench there... An awning; this summer heat can kill you...

Why is Vino taking so long? Why did I send a guy with a stammer? It must surely be adding at least twenty minutes on to the whole project.

And here comes Vino! When I see him pedalling up the road, I start thinking this was a bad move. And I'm hoping he didn't have a chance to ask Hilda. I'm hoping she wasn't at home. I'm hoping.

He parks the bike in the shade against the fence. But it seems he's taking forever. It's as if that stammer of his now also applies to getting off bikes and parking them. He's three feet from me, there's nobody around who might hear what he's got to say to me. Why can't he just come out with it?

As he gets off the bike he gives his back tyre a gentle kick and says: 'I didn't even n-notice how s-s-smooth...'

'Vino!'

He comes to stand against the other side of the gate. He looks at me and lets out a deep sigh. 'Bad news, bra,' he says.

'What did she say?'

'No, she can't go out with you.'

'But what were her words?' I don't know why I'm asking this; how many varieties of no do I want? 'Tell me exactly how it happened.'

'I go up to Hilda's house. She's outside cleaning the window sills or something. She wants to know if I came for the LP. I say no, I came to give her a message for her friend Janine. So I tell her.'

'Ja, but how did you say it?' I don't know what's wrong with me. I want direct speech not this she said he said stuff. And I get direct speech.

'I said, "You know my friend Chris?" She said, "Of course." I said, "He really likes your friend Janine. He wants to go out with her." She burst out laughing and said, "He must be joking."'

'Ja, but it's not for her to say...'

'But guess what?

'While we're talking there on the front stoep Janine arrives. Hilda tells Janine right there in front of me and Janine says, "Oh no, God no, not the clown."'

There it is. I wanted the details and I got the details. Vino can't help himself any more; he throws his head back and starts laughing. And I notice that he does have muistandjies after all. That little boy was right.

And about that garden? I don't think it's going to happen just yet.

So I'm a clown! I know what she's referring to – all those jokes I make in class, especially in Mr Garson's English lessons. If I have to describe myself, I see myself as a guy with a good sense of humour, a witty guy. A comedian. But definitely not a clown.

To get people to laugh a clown walks funny and pulls his face funny and falls flat on his face. I don't do that circus stuff, which, by the way, is called slapstick. But Janine or that Hilda would never know that. I've never heard them even trying to answer a quiz question.

And who does that Hilda think she is? When God handed out thighs she was somewhere on the minedumps so all she's ended up with are these two sticks. She also forgot to stand in line when God handed out smiles. So when we're all smiling or laughing what does she do? Sniff the air as if there's something rotten somewhere.

As for my sense of humour, I make puns and I think of funny things in a flash. I don't get monkeys in shorts to throw buckets of water at me.

I know there's nothing Vino can do about Janine not liking me. But the least he could have done was tell them I'm not a clown.

The day after the bad news my ma sends me up to Auntie June to return the five rand Ma borrowed from her. I have to go past Hilda's house. And as I approach, guess who's standing by the gate with Hilda? In the last two months I walk past her house and she's nowhere in sight. But now it's the day after the bad news and here she is. They spot me and they start doing that girl thing where they each hold one foot in the air and hold each other. I wish someone would tell girls that if they didn't hold that foot in the air they wouldn't have to hold onto each other.

As I pass them they both shout out at me, 'Howzit, clown!' and collapse into each other as they laugh.

Who are the clowns here, I wonder.

IT GOES WITHOUT saying that I'm not having a nice school break. I've become a heavy smoker, four per day. Vino, Conos and I sit around listening to our heavy metal records, Black Sabbath, The Greatest Show on Earth, Uriah Heep and Jimi Hendrix.

'I suppose they're going to tell all their friends,' I tell Vino.

He says, 'Maybe not.' But he knows I'm right.

At night I sit up late and read. I finish *The Outsider* by Albert Camus (it's pronounced Cimmoo–French is a very fancy language). It's a slim book, not even a hundred and fifty pages long, about a guy, Meursault, who prefers to be on his own and who doesn't care what people say or think about him. His mother dies and, even though he doesn't say it, you can tell he's not sad. The people around him talk behind his back about what a callous man he is. But I don't get the sense that he's callous. It's just the way he is–and he can't help it–take it or leave it.

This is one of the shortest books I've ever read. But it's made me think a lot. Camus believes in a philosophy called existentialism. His friend Jean Paul Sartre–also a writer–believes in the same thing. Basically, what it means is that life is meaningless. You are born, you go to school, go to varsity if you're white or go and work in a factory if you're coloured, get married, grow old, die.

I read more about Camus in encyclopaedias at the library. Camus lives in France but he was born in Algeria right here in Africa. And when he was a young man he used to be a goalkeeper for a local football team.

My father is also a goalkeeper. But one thing is for sure: my father is not an existentialist. If someone manages to put one past my father, a raw word explodes from his mouth.

Now this Camus guy, I'm wondering, if he were an existentialist did he actually try and stop the goals being scored against him. Because, think about it, if you're an existentialist then surely it doesn't matter whether you win or lose. Maybe he became an existentialist after he retired from football. But when he wrote the book he was an existentialist already. In that case why did he bother to write the book?

Anyway, I'm glad he wrote this book. My only problem is there's nobody that I can talk to about it. Vino and Conos and them are not interested. My ma reads a lot but mostly those Mills and Boons love stories. My father reads only the paper every night. Teachers? Mr Garson is far too busy and the rest are not one bit interested in literature.

Maybe everybody in Riverlea is an existentialist without actually knowing it.

I wish I were like Meursault. But I think I'm the direct opposite. And now I'm worried that Janine and Hilda are going to tell everybody about my proposal. No, they're not going to tell everybody, they'll just tell one friend; she'll tell another friend; that friend will tell her sister and so on. The next thing I know even the principal's wife is sniggering at me.

Coloureds don't have phones. But maybe that's because the government decided they don't need phones anyway.

When school re-opens I see the two girls on the playground. They spot me and I can see I'm going to have no peace.

'Clown!'

BUT PEACE DOES come unexpectedly on that very first day.

When we get to Mr Garson's class, he's sitting behind a pile of our exam scripts.

'Welcome back, class,' he says. 'I hope you've all had a good rest and that you are ready to face the term, with vigour, inspired by... I don't know, by all the books you've read.' He looks around and his eyes rest on me. 'Hey, Van Wyk?' he says.

I shrug. For once I don't have a witty remark for my favourite teacher. I could tell him about Camus, about Bernard Malamud's short story collection *The Magic Barrel*. But I know most of my classmates didn't touch a book and if I open my big mouth now it will sound like showing off. Besides you don't go and brag to your teacher while you're waiting for your English mark.

'Well,' he continues, 'if I look a little jaded, don't let it bother you too much. It's only because I spent the entire holidays going through this stack here.' He presses a finger down on our papers.

Mr Garson doesn't know it, but he always looks jaded, first day of school or last. But I like him, jaded look and all.

'I'm going to call out all your marks. But before I do that I want to announce the highest and the lowest. The highest: Chris, with eighty-eight per cent!'

Mr Garson gestures for me to stand up and I get up shyly while everybody applauds. Well, I'm not sure if it's everybody: those two sit far behind me so it will be stupid to look around at them. But what a good feeling. And then the good feeling gets even better.

Mr Garson calls out the lowest mark: 'Janine Jacobs with nineteen per cent.'

Now I look around. Straight at her.

The question 'Who's the clown now?' is written all over my face and even a nineteen percenter can read that.

But there's more. Mr Garson takes my essay from the top of the pile and tells me to read it to the class.

'And I want the prissy Ms Jacobs to listen carefully. Maybe Chris can teach her something that I can't.'

I look at Mr Garson. Does he know about me being in love with Janine? And about being called a clown? Teachers – especially ones like Mr Garson – see more than we think they do.

I would like to thank Mr Garson for stopping my humiliation. But I clear my throat and get ready to read 'Blue is the colour of my true love', which was inspired by my conversation about beads with Agnes:

Sipho, a handsome, athletic young man had left the rolling green hills of Natal to work in the gold mines of Johannesburg.

City Deep, in the city the miners call Egoli, was a harsh place to work. Three times a week a lift took Sipho and his workmates deep down into the bowels of the earth. And for the next six hours, in stifling subterranean tunnels they chipped away with their hammers to uncover the precious yellow streaks embedded between the grey and black rock.

Sipho was claustrophobic. Every day he felt sick and close to death as the lift took him down yet another time. But he was doing this for his beloved Thembi, whom he had left behind in a village in Natal.

'I will be back,' he had promised her. 'With money for the lobola and for our wedding. Will you wait for me, my love?'

She promised that she would wait for him, no matter how long it took.

But Egoli was not known for its gold only. There were gangsters in its streets, pickpockets and card sharps. And in its townships were shebeens that sold poisonous brews, and women of easy virtue who declared their love for you as they slid their long fingers into your pockets.

Sibongile, a beauty from Soweto, fluttered her mascara'd eyes at Sipho, and he was spellbound.

'You must leave Thembi,' Sibongile said. 'You are mine now.' She bought a necklace of red and black beads one day and presented it to Sipho.

'Does this mean it is over between us?'

'No,' she said. 'They are for Thembi. Send the necklace to her. Or I will — from you.'

Then tragedy struck like a lightning bolt. A rockfall at City Deep trapped a team of miners in a shaft deep down. Of the twenty-six men, all were rescued except two. One of those killed was Sipho.

A tearful Sibongile undertook to travel to Thembi's village in Natal to break the news.

Thembi was inconsolable, tears streaming down her lovely face. 'I loved him so much,' she told the bearer of this sad news.

'He loved you too,' Sibongile said. She took out of her bag the necklace of white and blue beads that he had given her. 'Before he died he asked me to give you this.'

Farewell to Agnes

When I come from school in the afternoons I usually find Agnes in the lounge. The radio is tuned to Radio Zulu and she is sitting there on the couch listening, her head bent as if she's staring at a spot on her lap.

I have my usual daily list of questions, but I have to wait until the radio drama is over. I have also promised her that I will teach her to write in English. But that was a long time ago, and we haven't spoken about it since.

Agnes is probably the only person from Soweto I know. Apartheid does its job with precision, separating us from each other. What I know about the people in Soweto is what I read about in the *Golden City Post* on Sundays.

There's Orlando Pirates from Orlando and Moroka Swallows from Moroka. And Pirates seem to win all the time.

I ask Agnes about her family. She has a husband and a son called Vusi.

I ask her about Vusi all the time in the hope that she will tell me something interesting about him – that Vusi is a champion sprinter, or a mathematics wizard, or once killed a poisonous snake with his bare hands. She has nothing to tell me.

But I don't give up. If she won't tell me anything about the Amazing Vusi from Mofolo North, then I want to meet him and see for myself.

'Agnes, can you bring Vusi with you one day, I'd like to meet him.'

'What for?'

'I want to be friends with him.'

'Serious?'

'Ja,' I nod.

'But you have enough friends – Conos, Vinos, those boys next door.'

'But why can't Vusi be my friend?'

She sighs. 'He lives in Soweto, you live here.' It's impractical, is what she's trying to say.

'We'll make a plan.'

Agnes laughs and goes back to laying her eggs and hatching her chickens.

But I don't give up. I nag and nag and nag some more. It works, and eventually, one sunny morning during our school holidays, Agnes arrives with Vusi and presents him to me. He's a chubby boy, younger and shorter than me, dressed in khaki shorts and shirt.

'Hi Vusi.' I greet my new friend and extend my hand.

He looks down at my hand, puzzled. His mother tells him something in Zulu, and he shakes my hand.

'So how you keeping, how's school?'

Agnes again plays interpreter. He gives her an answer and she says, 'He says it's OK. But I don't think he goes to school any more.'

'Why not?'

'He goes to caddy for white people on the golf course.'

I nod and smile at Vusi, and he nods back. And that's more or less what we do all morning – me trying to be Vusi's friend, him thinking about the golf course and all the tips he's missing.

And what about the thousands of other people in Soweto? What do they do on weekends? Quite the same as coloureds, it seems: the shebeens fill up, there's drinking, dancing and quite often a knife fight that ends in death.

ONE DAY WHEN I come home from school, Agnes thrusts a leaflet into my hands.

'What's this?' I ask her.

'Politics,' she says dramatically.

I've been asking her lots of political questions lately. Did she ever meet or see Nelson Mandela or Walter Sisulu before they went to prison?

'You can't talk about that,' she wrings her hands and shakes her head and walks away.

I laugh.

'You don't believe me,' she says with foreboding.

'I do believe you, Agnes…'

'If the police hear you they come and lock you up.'

'I know,' I tell her, following her to the kitchen. 'But there's no police here now. Maybe it's dangerous to talk on a train or in a pass office…'

'You can't talk about Nelson Mandela in a pass office.' Her eyes are big with indignation.

I give up.

So today, maybe out of contrition, she is the one who first utters the dreaded word 'politics'.

'Where did you get this leaflet, Agnes?'

'At the train station this morning.'

'Thanks.' I smile at her and sit in the lounge and read. It's in English and Zulu, a call by the Sofasonke Party to all the residents of Soweto to attend a meeting. Top of the agenda will be the housing shortage.

Without asking Agnes I know that this Sofasonke Party must be approved by the government. A party that cannot elect a government or the country's Prime Minister, a bunch of men who advise the government on local issues: the housing shortage, crime in the streets, lack of electrification, not enough schools here, too many shebeens there.

The coloureds also have such parties: the Labour Party, the National Party, the Federal Party. They meet in some government 'kitchen' somewhere and call themselves the CRC, the Coloured Representative Council, and report to the white Minister of Coloured Affairs.

'What does "Sofasonke" mean?' I ask Agnes, thinking that it is probably Zulu for 'Labour' or 'United'.

Agnes is scrubbing the kitchen floor. She looks up at me and thinks for a moment. 'We all die together…' she says.

'What are you talking about?'

'You ask me the name, I give you the name,' she says, smiling at my bewilderment. 'Now get out of my way. I've got eggs to lay…'

'We all die together,' I say it out loud. It sounds like a party that means business, that either gets what it wants or dies trying.

AGNES IS STILL working for us when I finish school and go to work, and write my first batch of poems on my way to becoming a writer. And when the police come to take me away for an afternoon to be interrogated – the first of several times.

And then Agnes is gone, to work somewhere else where the pay is better – her wages were forty-four rands per month, no worse or better than any of the other housekeepers in the townships. There are no tears, no hugs, no kisses.

She had come four or five years ago when there were four Van Wyk children. She left when there were two more, Nicolette and Russel.

I don't even miss her much at first – I am preoccupied with another life: girls, reading, looking for work, politics. But every now and then something reminds me of her.

Like the time I read about James Mpanza. It's one of those fascinating township stories that the world has forgotten, and it goes something like this:

James Mpanza was a Zulu, born in Zululand in 1891.

When he was in his early twenties he went to a general dealer's shop, robbed the shopkeeper and set fire to the store, razing it to the ground. When the fire was eventually put out, there was nothing left. Stock, furniture, counter, everything was smoke and ash.

And where was the store owner? Nobody knew.

But a determined detective crawled through the ashes looking for the man's remains – and eventually found them with the help of, of all things, a tea strainer, scooping up a burnt out knee cap, a knuckle, a toe.

The detective also managed to track down the murderer, one James Mpanza.

The young Mpanza stood trial and was sentenced to death for robbery and murder. But he wasn't hanged. In 1927 Prince Albert paid a visit to Natal, part of his mommy's empire, and pardoned all the criminals on death row.

Mpanza's sentence was commuted to many years in prison. He was sent down to a prison in Joburg and a decade or so later he was set free.

It is now the 1930s. Mpanza's youth has been spent in the dust and stench of various prisons and he is a stocky man living in the dust and stench of a slum called Doornfontein.

There is not yet a place called Soweto. But soon there will be, and Mpanza will have a lot to say and do about it.

The apartheid government comes to power in 1948. The first thing it does is separate all the races into Bantu (black), coloured (mixed race), Indian and white.

The Bantu, it decides, should all go and live in their various homelands. Zulus to Zululand, Tswanas to Bophuthatswana, Vendas to Venda, Xhosas to the Transkei and so on.

When this law is passed almost all black people in South Africa finds themselves about a thousand kilometres from where they're supposed to be. But the government needs them to work in the gold mines, and in white homes. And so some black people are allowed to live in the urban areas such as Johannesburg. And Soweto is built.

A few hundred families move in. But a few thousand are left on the waiting list. Before anyone can blink, these families on the waiting list have taken up residence in the yards of existing homes.

The white government never solves the housing problem and James Mpanza becomes a champion of the homeless – with his Sofasonke Party.

In the mid-seventies the Sofasonke Party is still fighting for housing. The party hands out pamphlets to commuters at a Soweto train station. A black woman takes one and saves it for a curious coloured boy who's forever asking her questions.

Trouble in the eighties

I think about Agnes a lot in the eighties. There is so much unrest in the townships – actually it is called unrest by the authorities, but it is really the beginning of the end of the racist apartheid government before the ANC came to power.

There are petrol bombs and housing protests, police patrolling the townships and even fighting between the ANC and Inkatha supporters.

In Johannesburg's East Rand township of Thokoza, knife- and knobkierie-wielding thugs come in the night and chase entire families out of their homes.

Where is Agnes, I wonder. And what is she doing now? Is she safe?

A publisher of easy-to-read books for adults commissions me to write a small easy book for their Adult Basic Education series.

I remember how I had always promised Agnes that I would teach her to read. And, duly inspired, I write this little book called *My name is Selina Mabiletsa*. This is the story – with only a chapter or two and a drawing on every page and a word list at the back explaining difficult words such as 'worry', 'crayon' and 'proud':

My name is Selina Mabiletsa
Selina Mabiletsa and her husband Joe lived in a small house in Thokoza. They had many friends and they were happy.

Selina could not read or write, but this did not worry her. Joe could read. He read the newspaper to Selina. He also read letters to her.

'Joe is my eyes,' Selina always said.

One day Selina's eyes closed forever.

Joe got very sick. He went to hospital. And he died.

Selina cried for many days. One day she stopped crying. She said: 'Selina, you must be strong. You must stop crying. You must start living again.'

The next day Selina went to a school where adults learned to read and write. She began to learn to read and write.

Selina tried to write her name. This was hard. Selina wrote the words. But she always got them wrong.

One night Selina was lying in bed. Something good happened. Selina saw her name in her mind. She wanted to write it down. Selina found a crayon. But she had no paper. So she wrote on the wall in big words:

My name is Selina Mabiletsa

Selina was a proud woman.

Then war came to Thokoza. People were fighting in the streets. People died in the streets. Cars and buses burned. Shops burned. Houses burned. Selina's house burned!

Selina and her friends went to live in the veld. They built zinc houses. The houses were very cold in winter. In summer they were very hot.

Selina stopped going to school. Sometimes she wished she was dead.

After a year there was good news. The government was going to fix the burned out houses in Thokoza.

Everybody talked about this, but Selina did not believe them. So she went to see for herself.

It was true! Builders were putting new roofs on the houses. They were hanging on new doors. Soon the houses were almost like new again.

Selina went to move back into her house. The TV people were there. The newspaper people were there. Everybody wanted to see this happy moment.

Then Selina got a shock. She saw two men standing at the door of her house.

'You must show us that you lived here,' one of the men said. 'Please show us your papers.'

Selina knew nothing about papers. She picked up her bags and began to walk away.

Then she remembered something.

'I can show you that this is my house,' she said.

Selina walked into the house and the people followed her. She walked into her bedroom.

Selina pointed to the writing on the wall. A year had gone by, but it was still there:

My name is Selina Mabiletsa

Elvis

It's 1990. Early autumn. I'm in my early thirties. I've been married for eight years and Kathy and I have two sons, Kevin, at school, and Karl, still in nappies and being looked after by my mother.

We have our own house in Riverlea. It's bigger and more comfortable than the house I grew up in: spacious, carpeted rooms, a long, wide passage.

We bought the house from a family that went to live in Australia. They decided that the blacks were coming to power any day now, and they wanted to avoid that.

Quite frankly I'm happy the blacks have put the fear of God into them. I like this house, the price was good and I can't wait for the new government to kick in. Why anyone would want to give up the most momentous moment in Africa's history for boomerangs and kangaroos I just don't know. But good luck to them.

Miriam is our housekeeper. She is a Sotho woman from the Free State, exactly the same age as Kathy and me. Even though I insist that she calls us by our first names, she calls Kathy Mme (mother) and me Ntate (father). At first I resist it, but she won't stop.

Miriam has two children from two different men. I don't know anything about Patricia's father. Elvis's father, Moses, was going to marry Miriam but changed his mind. He's a schoolteacher at a primary school in Ladybrand.

The Van Wyks meet Patricia and Elvis during the December school holidays. Poor Patricia, she's failed Standard Seven again and for this her mother welcomes her to Joburg with a smack. Patricia is a stick figure of a girl, quiet and brooding.

She helps her mother clean the house, washes the dishes, sweeps the kitchen and then sits down on the back stoep awaiting further instructions. Vacuums the lounge, sits down. Even though her surroundings are new, she shows no curiosity.

Elvis is different. He's a chubby nine year old running all over the place. He speaks to me in Sesotho and even though I don't respond, he persists. He seems to believe that it will all suddenly come to me and that I'll start chatting any minute now.

He also tries this on Kathy, Kevin, Karl and our Alsatian Danger.

He finds some of Karl's old toys and plays with them for an hour or so until he grows tired of the bits of Lego and plastic cars.

He finds toy sunglasses and wears them around the house.

Elvis gets at least one whipping a day from his mother. But it doesn't seem to deter him from running around and causing trouble. Every time I see the poor little guy being attacked by his mother, I run and grab whatever weapon she has in her hands.

'Stop hitting him!' I shout at her.

'But he's naughty, he's rude!' she shouts back.

One late morning I look up from my work to see Miriam on the other side of the window. She's on a ladder and I can hear the window squeaking as she gives it that magical dry newspaper rub. Also making delighted noises, there in the background, is Elvis. He's fully recovered from his most recent beating and he's chasing Danger around a tree.

This is nice and peaceful. God is smiling down on the coloureds, the Sothos, the dogs… But I know it won't last. And of course God blinks.

At some point little Elvis stops playing with Danger. He looks around for a change of action. He spies his ma on the ladder rubbing vigorously at a bedroom window. Her big bum is wobbling up and down as she rubs.

Elvis approaches. He takes hold of the ladder with both hands and starts shaking it.

'Elvis!' she screams. 'Stop it!'

For some reason Elvis thinks this is a big joke and that maybe his ma will soon see the funny side. He shakes more vigorously and Miriam comes crashing down into the agapanthus bush.

I hear the commotion from inside my study. I run to the window and see Miriam, huge branch in hand, closing in on a screaming Elvis who is scampering around the tree in much the same way as Danger was doing earlier. Danger himself is adding to the noise with hysterical barking.

I run out the front door and into the yard to once again rescue Elvis from another beating.

'No no no,' I tell Miriam, yanking the branch out of her hand.

'I'll kill him!' she yells.

He's cowering behind the tree, frightened but alert, in case she breaks loose from my grip. Why does he catch on this stuff when he knows he's going to get a hiding, I wonder. But it's for this that I like him. He's a likeable bundle of mischief, finding out how the world works while his sister sits and stares into a dark space.

ONE DAY, A few weeks after Patricia and Elvis have gone back to their grandparents in the Free State, Miriam comes into the lounge where I'm writing. She has a problem and needs my help.

'Ntate.'

'Ja.'

'You know Elvis?'

'Memphis or Ladybrand?'

'Ntate?'

'Your son?'

'Ja.'

'What about him?'

'His father Moses, he doesn't pay me the money for Elvis.'

'What money?'

'The money. We went to the court there in Ladybrand and the magistrate said he must pay me a hundred and twenty rand per month. He must put it in my account. It's for clothes for that child, and for food.'

Moses is not paying his maintenance. Riverlea is full of these men. They're the ones who stroll into the shebeens and bars, push out their chests, and say: 'My third girlfriend just gave birth to my fourth child. I'm a man!'

But ask him if he's buying clothes and formula for the newborn, and whether he has a plan for the child's education? He'll look at you as if you're from a different planet.

'Why are you telling me this, Miriam? What am I supposed to do?'

'Aw, Ntate!' she says surprised. 'I want you to take me to the court to explain.'

'In the Free State!'

'No, here in Joburg. And then the Joburg magistrate can phone that one in the Free State and tell him. And then they can fetch Moses...'

'Hey, hey, hey!' I hold my hand up to stop her. 'You have to go to Ladybrand yourself. I'll give you three days off, a week off. Full pay. Just go there and sort it out yourself.'

'Aw, Ntate.'

'Miriam, listen. It's not that I can't help you. But it's a Free State problem, not a Joburg problem. I'll go there to the magistrate's court and sit in a queue for five hours, three days in a row. They'll send me to room one hundred, and then to counter eight and then to fill in a hundred forms in triplicate and after all that some official will tell me, "This are not our problem – thenk you dankie."'

Miriam is not in a laughing mood. She goes back to her work and I go back to mine.

But I can't concentrate. She's spraying furniture polish on to the tables and chairs and it's as if Mr Min is calling to me, 'Psst-psst, help her, help her.'

I look up from time to time and I can see her. And I know

she's not happy – in fact she's angry. And if Moses were here now she'd take a stick to the man and give him a good beating. I've seen her do that, not only to little Elvis. One or two guys here in Riverlea rubbed her up the wrong way and limped away.

'Dammit,' I mumble under my breath. Miriam looks up.

I call her.

'Where does he teach?'

She gives me the name of the school.

'Do you have the school's phone number?'

'Ja.'

I tell her to fetch it. She doesn't have to, it's in her head. She rattles it off and I write it down.

I ask her for his full names and surname and a few other details.

'Sit down, Miriam.' She sits on a chair opposite me, Mr Min in one hand, a cloth in the other.

'I'm going to phone him right now. You can listen but you mustn't say a word. Don't even make a noise. Just listen, OK.'

'OK.'

I dial the number and the principal answers.

'Good afternoon, Mr Moerane,' I say in my Afrikaans accent. 'Sorry to disturb, sir. But may I speak wif Thabiso Moses Maseko.'

Miriam suppresses a giggle. Meanwhile Mr Moerane wastes no time getting my man to the phone.

Within minutes I hear, 'Good afternoon, sir,' slightly out of breath.

'Is that Thabiso Moses Maseko?' I ask.

'Yes, sir.'

'You are speaking wif Louis Jordaan. I am the Director General in the Department of Social Welfare.'

'Yes, sir.'

'Now, by law, law number one hundred and sixty-six slash forty-four, whenever addressing a gentleman of any colour, be he white or black, I have to refer to him as sir. This is a new law. You follow?'

'Yes, sir.'

'But I would like to call you a piece of rubbish, you follow?'

'Yes, sir.'

'And that is on account of you not paying your maintenance fees for one little boy viz your son Elvis, you understand me?'

'Sir, I am going to…'

'Shut up and listen!'

'Yes, sir.'

'I have a warrant out for your arrest. But Ladybrand is not my jurisdiction and so I have to fill out two forms – a PFN 17 and a TD 41. Then I have to apply for a travel expenses voucher to fly down to the Free State, handcuff you in your classroom and fly you back up here. Then I put you in jail and apply to the prosecutor not to let you out until you stand trial in six months' time…'

'Sir… sir please…'

'You'll get your chance, Thabiso. Please don't interrupt, I am a busy man; I have eggs to lay and chickens to hatch, you follow?'

'I follow, sir.'

And Miriam is following too. Her eyes big, her mouth wide open, she's trying hard not to laugh as she pictures him out there in Ladybrand, the phone rattling away in his hands.

'So, to save me the trouble, Mr Moses, father of Elvis, I'm asking you to kindly put that money in Mrs Sealoma's bank account.'

'I will, sir.'

'When?'

'Today, sir.'

'And every month.'

'Every month, sir.'

Moses Maseko proved to be a man of his word.

Eggs to lay, chickens to hatch

So here I am, sitting at our dining room table, trying to write a short story and listening to my favourite music. It's not the heavy metal of my youth (Black Sabbath, Uriah Heep and The Greatest Show on Earth have all been packed away and are gathering dust somewhere). My 'new' music is ironically many decades older than that heavy metal of the late sixties and seventies.

It's jazz.

I've heard this music before: in my early teens, on a late Saturday afternoon, *The Lexington Big Band Show*, the DJ announces in a deep drawl. The trumpets and clarinets and drums of Bennie Goodman, the Tommy Dorsey Orchestra and Glen Miller fill the lounge. I hear it but I don't listen. Maybe it's because I associate it with parents and grandparents, and with a forgotten time long long ago.

Once Agnes tried to tell me about Glen Miller. I waved dismissively at her, saying, 'That trumpet stuff, no thanks.'

There were men and women and older boys who did play jazz LPs every now and then. On the corner of Flinders Street was one such boy, Frankie, many years my senior. I recall Saturday afternoons, his friends in the lounge, chatting and laughing, drinking beer, and Ellington, Coltrane and Miles Davis entertaining.

On the way to the shops for Ma, I'd stop and listen. Why do they like it so much? What is it that I'm missing? I'd listen for a while to try and get it. But I never did.

My father was a jazz lover. But he never thought it important enough to pass it on to us. Apparently his stepmother bought him dozens of records. But when he got married and packed up his LPs, she said, 'Hold it right there. Those stay here.'

And, like the grandfather clock in the folksong, 'The jazz stopped, never to go again'. But I never gave up. And in a way it never gave up on me. Everywhere I looked and listened, books, TV, conversations with friends, in history, politics, culture, it was there.

So I bought a CD called *Most Requested Songs* by Duke Ellington. It's got everybody's favourites, I thought. If I don't like this I never will. I listened to 'In a mellow tone', 'Take the A Train' and 'Satin Doll'. Now I have a new problem at home: where will I find space for my jazz CDs – over two hundred and growing!

Like Depeche Mode, 'I just can't get enough'.

A few years ago, I sat glued to BBC TV watching a documentary on the history of jazz. For several Saturdays in a row, all the old masters of the art were paraded before my fascinated eyes and ears – Ella Fitzgerald, Sarah Vaughn, Louis Armstrong, Duke Ellington, Horace Silver, Gerry Mulligan, Nat King Cole, Miles Davis.

One Saturday I watch a clip, black and white and grainy, dug up from the 1940s. The band is called Louis Jordan and the Tympany Five and they're singing a song called 'Caldonia'. Songs about women are usually a tribute to their beauty. But in this song, all Mr Louis Jordan wants to know is, 'Caldonia, what makes your big feet so big?'

It makes me laugh and a week or two later I have a whole box set of five Louis Jordan CDs – including, for my amusement, Caldonia and her big feet. But there are virtually dozens of lovely 'new' old tunes to listen to. And a surprise awaits me – the surprise that will inspire me to write this book.

One afternoon, I take out my Louis Jordan CDs. I slip one of them into my CD player and listen as I work. The songs are amusing and catchy and many of them are so infectious that they distract me from my work. Then one song proves to be more than just distracting. It makes me sit bolt upright and turn up the volume.

It's a song about a Farmer Brown who one night hears a noise in his hen house. It must be a fox or something come to raid my hen house, he says crossly. So he takes his gun and goes to investigate.

He gets there to find that there is no fox and that everything is in order. In fact, he's disturbed his fowls who, irritated at having their sleep disturbed, yell out to him:

There ain't nobody here but us chickens
There ain't nobody here at all
So calm yourself and stop that fuss
There ain't nobody here but us.
Tomorrow is a busy day
We got things to do, we got eggs to lay
We got ground to dig and worms to scratch
It takes a lot of sittin' gettin' chicks to hatch

It took a lot of sitting, dearest Agnes. But eventually the eggs did hatch.

Glossary

abba	to be carried on a woman's back
Ai die donkey is 'n wonderlike ding	Ah the donkey is a wonderful thing
ai junne!	oh Jeeze!
amagoduka	those who are on the move
apie skaapie	monkey sheepie
arra	watch out, be careful
awu batho	ah people
baba	father
babalaas	hangover
baie dankie	thanks a lot
bakbene	bandy legs
bakkie	a small van
bedryf	industry
blikskottel	tin dish
bloed	blood
boerewors	a type of sausage
Boesman	Bushman (derogatory term for coloured person)
boeta	brother
chommies	buddies
brak (brakkie)	mongrel
brandsiekte	mange
braskap	brotherhood, brotherliness
bredie	stew

deurmekaar	(literally, 'through each other') confused or confusing
dhunia	coriander
Die Bybel	The Bible
doek	headscarf
Een klein stappie oppie maan, een groot stappie virrie manne	One small step on the moon, one big step for the men
eina	ouch
En ek vat nie kak nie	and I don't take shit
fahfee	a Chinese gambling game
finish and klaar	absolutely finished, done or completed
frikkadels	meatballs
gatjie klip	(literally, 'hole and stone'), a game played with pebbles by girls
gee stuk	gimme a piece
Gee stuk, nix dols, nix mangas	a playground ritual in which, if you have your fingers crossed no one can ask you for some of your lunch
gwarra	tease
heilige	holy
here, hemel	lord, heavens
Hoor wat vra die kind my nou?	Hear what this child is asking me now?
jiet	dance party
jislaaik	gee whiz
kaalgat peach	naked peach (nectarine)
kabawo	my father's son (Xhosa)
kalkoen	turkey
kekeleza	pretending to work when you're hungover
kennekie	a children's street game
kirriebekke	a children's game played in the street

klap	slap
kwaai	smart or dangerous
kwela-kwela	police van ('pick up' in Zulu)
laaitie	youngster
larnie	a white or rich person
Lekker Lollies	an ice sucker
lobola	brideprice
mageu	a non-alcoholic, home-brewed drink made of thin, slightly fermented maize meal porridge
miesies	madam
moegoe	weakling
my ma hoor my	my mother hears me
net blankes	whites only
nooit	never
oe genade	oh mercy
ouchie	the hero in a Western
ouens	guys
pasella	a small gift of a sweet from a shopkeeper
piskarretjie	pee car
sies	sis
skinder	gossip
skop	kick
skorokoro	jalopy; a car that just about works
skrik	fright
skyf	a few puffs of a cigarette
smaak	like
snot en trane	snot and tears
sommer	just like that, suddenly
spy	weakling
spy-bek	gossipmonger
sticks	pay a fare for a friend
stoep	small step by a door

stompie	cigarette butt
strokie	a stroke of luck when a shopkeeper gives you too much change by mistake
tamaletjie	a flat, round, homemade sweet
tannie	aunt, but mother in township parlance
tekere	go crazy
toppie	father
trap	tramp
tsotsi	thug or gangster
veld	field
vetkoek	fatcake; a greasy cake usually stuffed with mince
voetsek	used to chase away a dog
zip	keep quiet

Acknowledgements

It must surely give you the weirdest feeling: you're in the middle of something important with colleagues or children when the phone rings and it's your brother Chris: 'What was So-and-so's dog's name?' he wants to know. Or: 'Whose granny had a beard?' 'What was that guy Kevin singing to their housekeeper when he was caught playing truant at home?' 'What was the colour of the beret Agnes always wore?'

My brothers Derek and Shaune, and sisters Alison and Nicolette have had to put up with these and other stranger questions for the last two years. I thank them for scratching their heads for me and casting their minds back as they helped me recall my story.

My wife Kathy too, had to tolerate some very strange indulgences – like me bursting into our bedroom just as she was about to fall asleep, asking her please to recite an old skipping-rope song from a time when she was one of those girls who danced to 'Daar onder by dam' in the dusty streets of Riverlea, in those magical bygone days when streets were longer, yards bigger, the teachers cleverer, the shopkeepers more intimidating, the minedumps higher.

In the telling of these stories I would begin sometimes with the tale of a dog and end up with something I once heard on the radio. My editor Andrea Nattrass would shake me out of my little reverie with a gentle but firm: 'Dog or radio?' to keep me from wandering. And that's apart from all the inconsistencies and typos that she weeded out.

And then came Sally Hines to make absolutely sure they were all gone.

Gerald de Villiers didn't mind reading the manuscript a second and third time to make sure there was more than enough laughter – and fewer girlfriends than he had in his teenage years.

To all of you, my grateful thanks. Now, whenever I recall the stories of my childhood, I will remember you too.